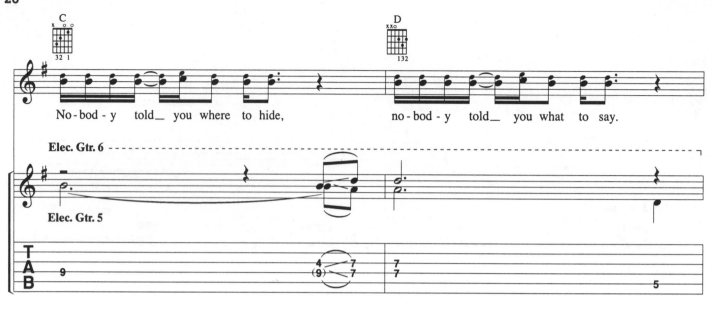

No-bod-y told___ you where to hide, no-bod-y told___ you what to say.

No one showed___ you where to turn, showed you when___ to run a-way. Can you

D.S. % al Coda

Coda

shoved it in___ my face,_____ this pain___ you gave___ to me._____

Just take it all___ a - way,___ this pain you gave___ to me.___

Elec. Gtr. 1

Take it all___ a - way,___ this pain you gave___ to me.___

Acous. Gtr. 2

Acous. Gtr. 1

Elec. Gtr. 1 tacet

Elec. Gtr. 1 *harm.

*Harmonics on Acous. Gtr. 1 only.

Born Again

Words and Music by James Walsh, James Stelfox, Barry Westhead and Benjamin Byrne

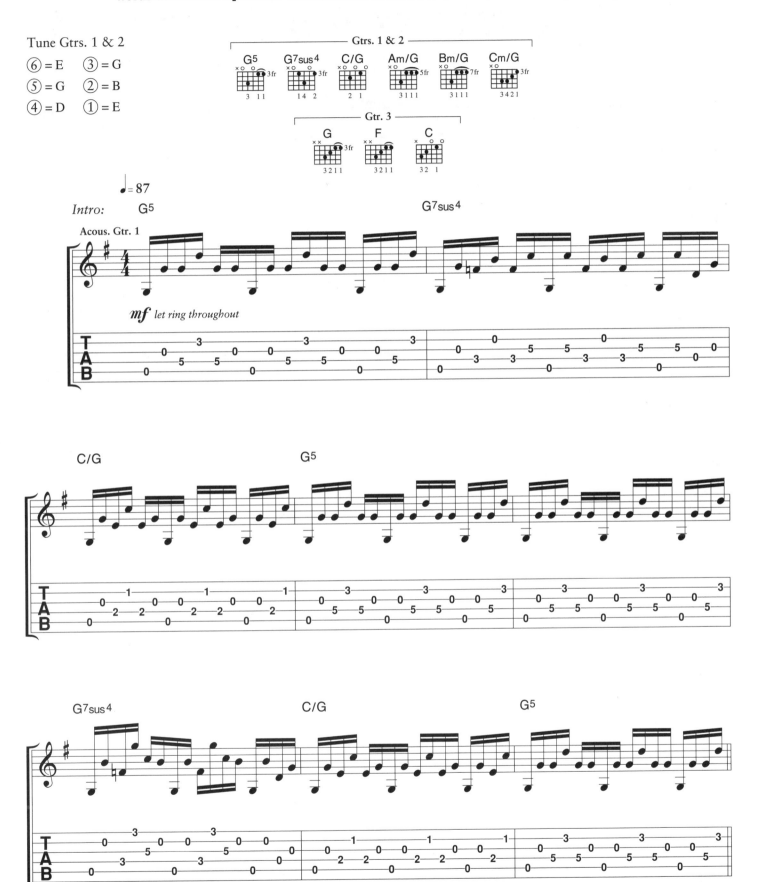

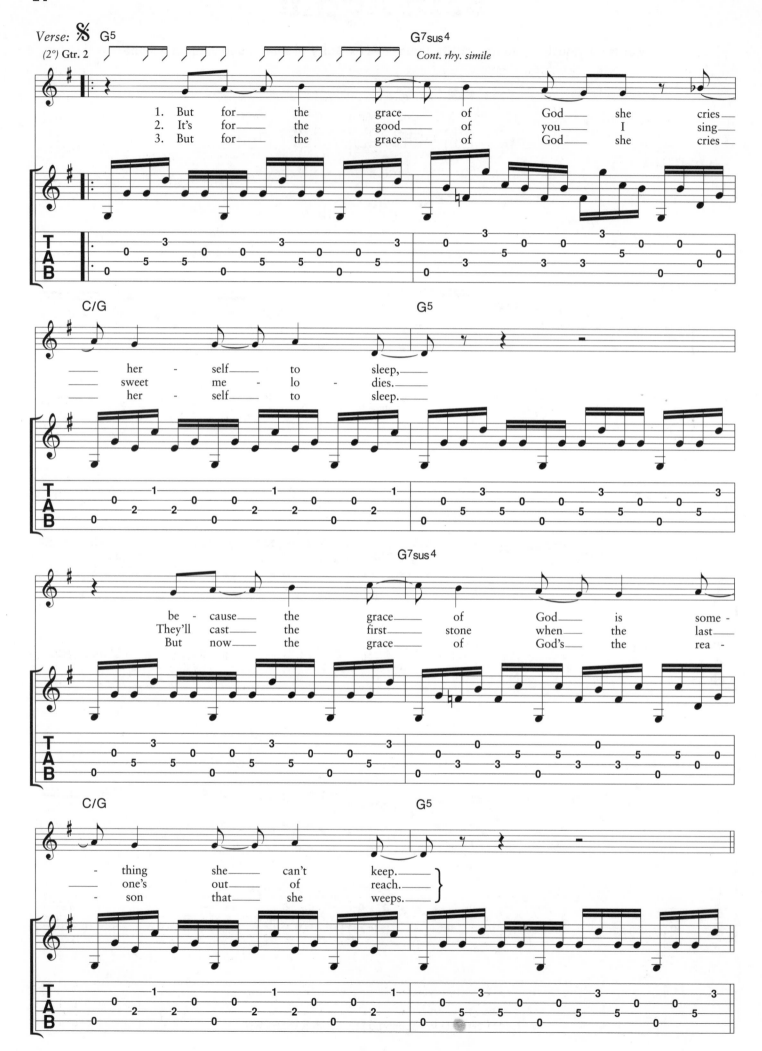

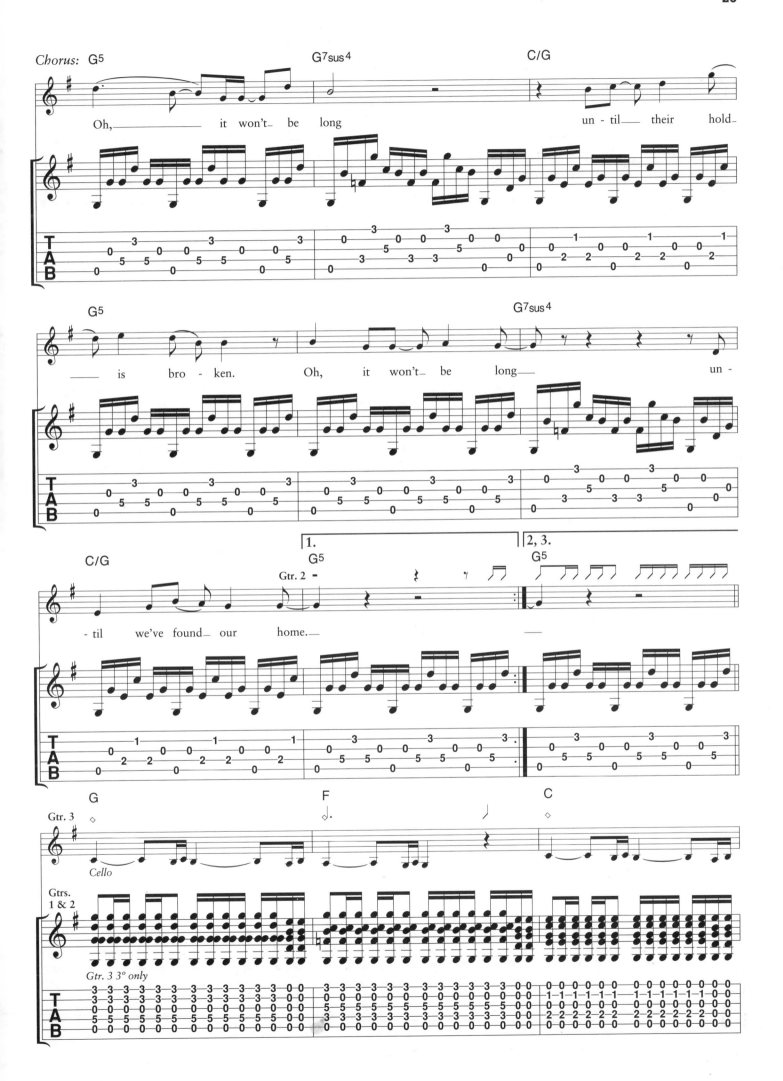

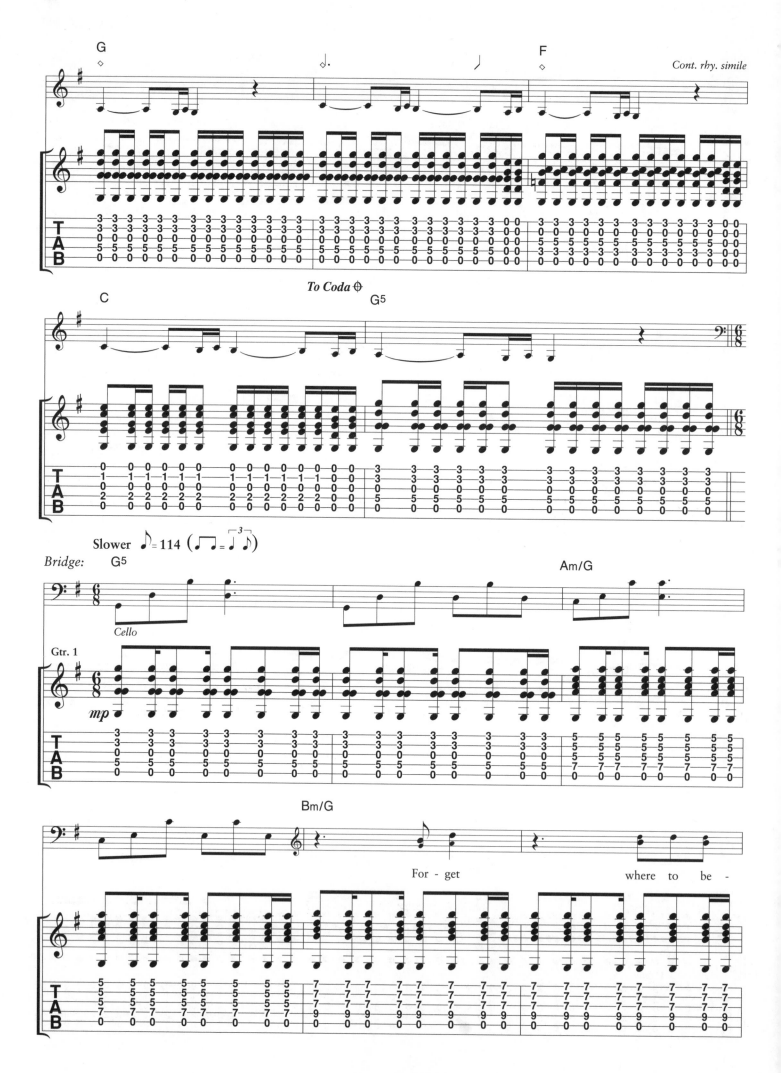

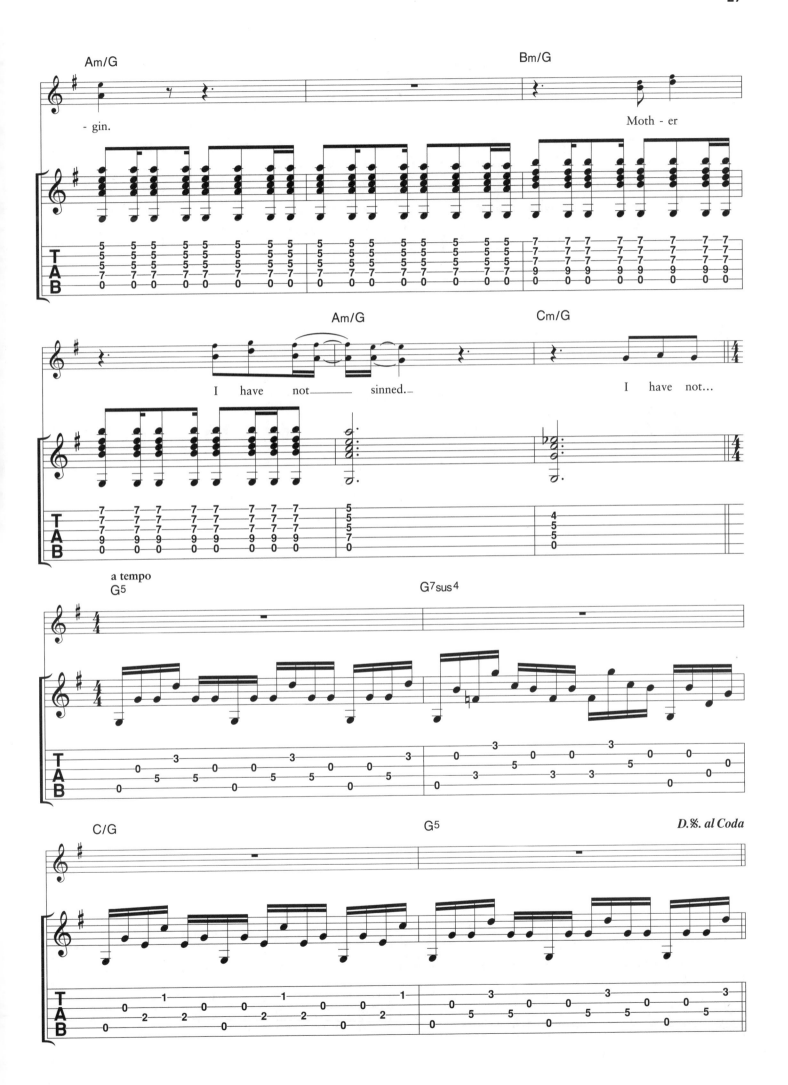

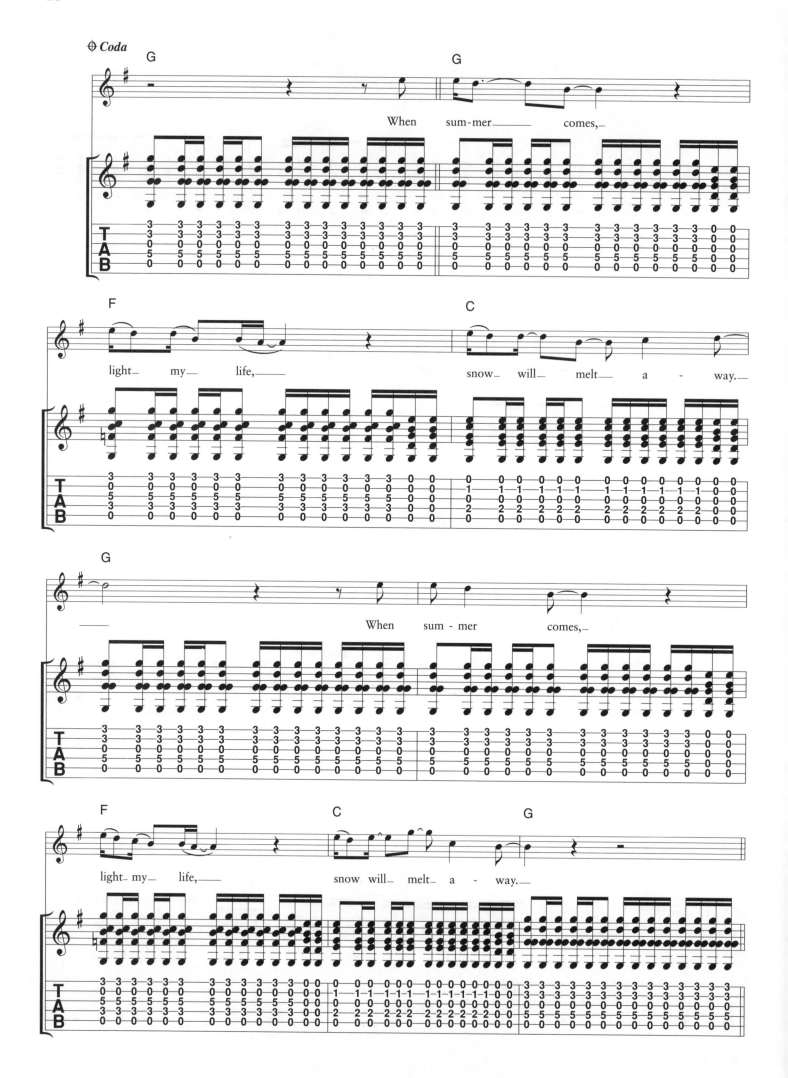

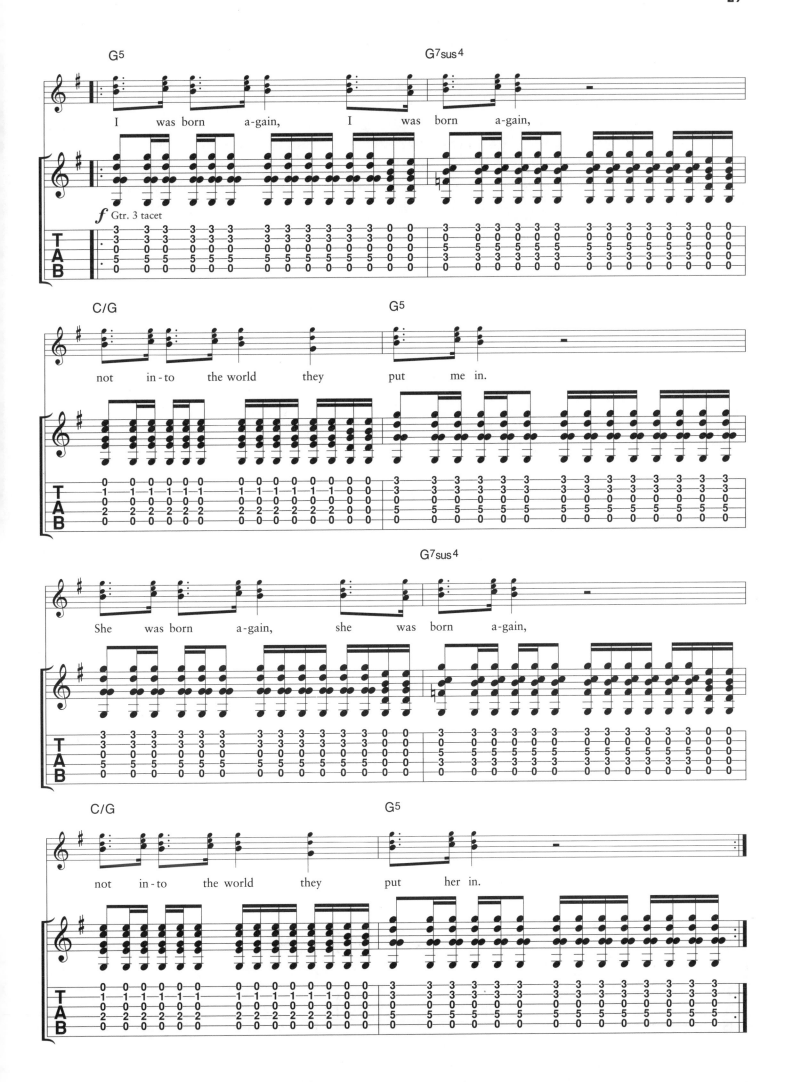

Can You Dig It?

Words and Music by Martin Coogan

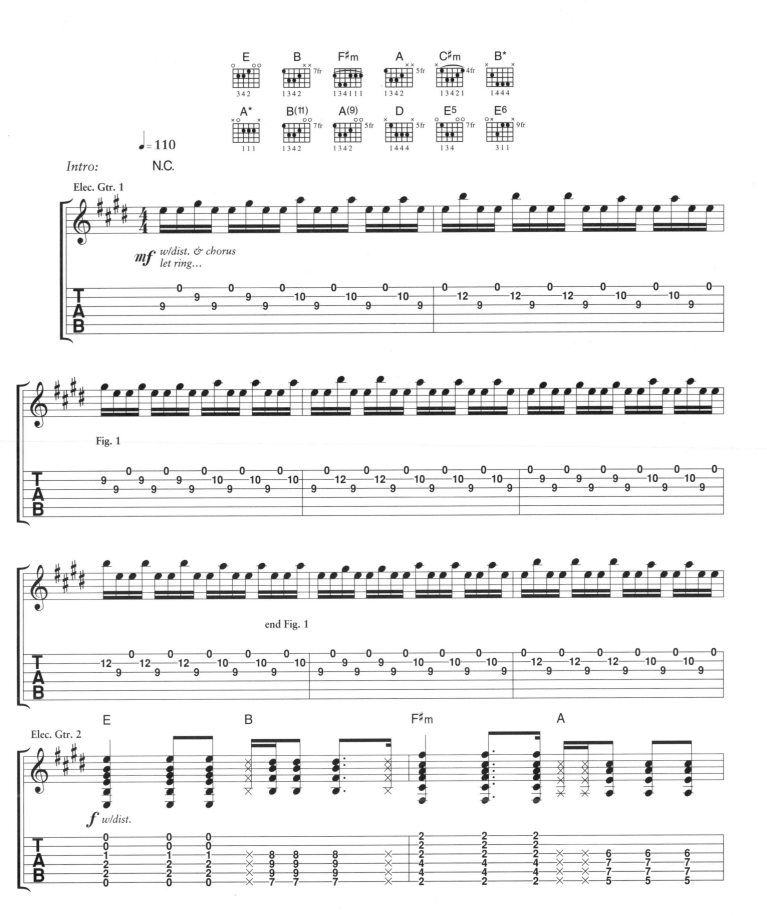

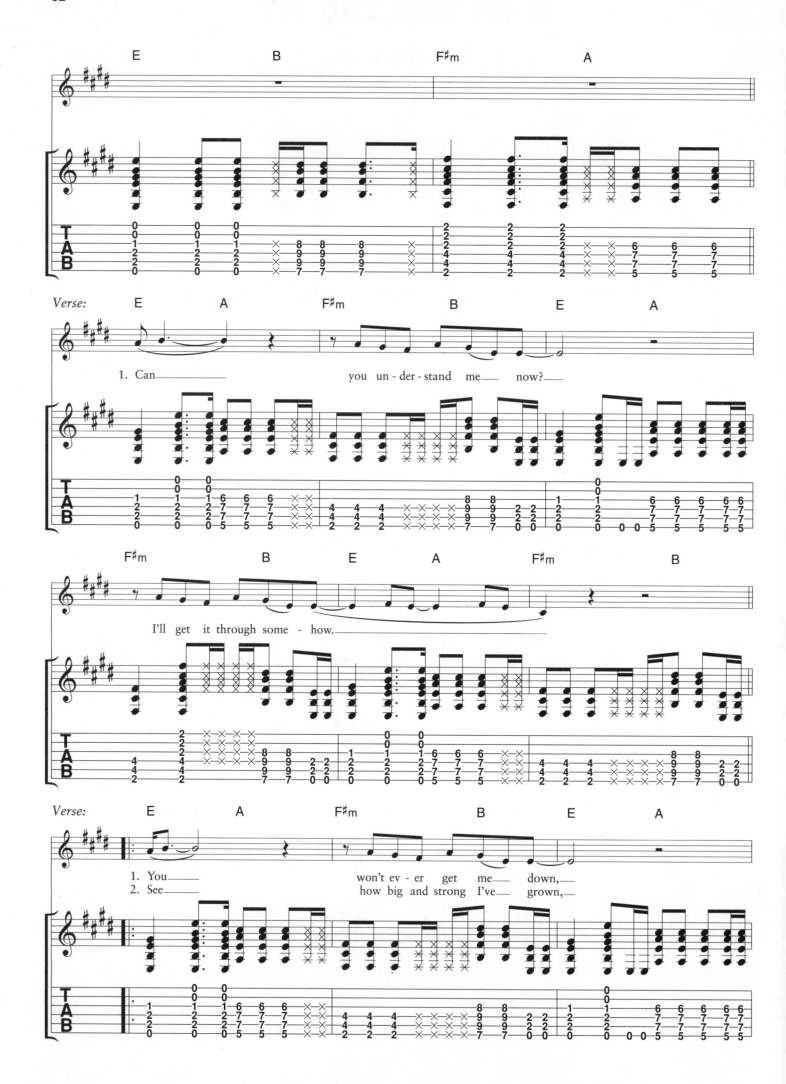

Dreaming Of You

Words and Music by James Skelly

Solo:

Empty At The End

Words and Music by Tom White and Alex White

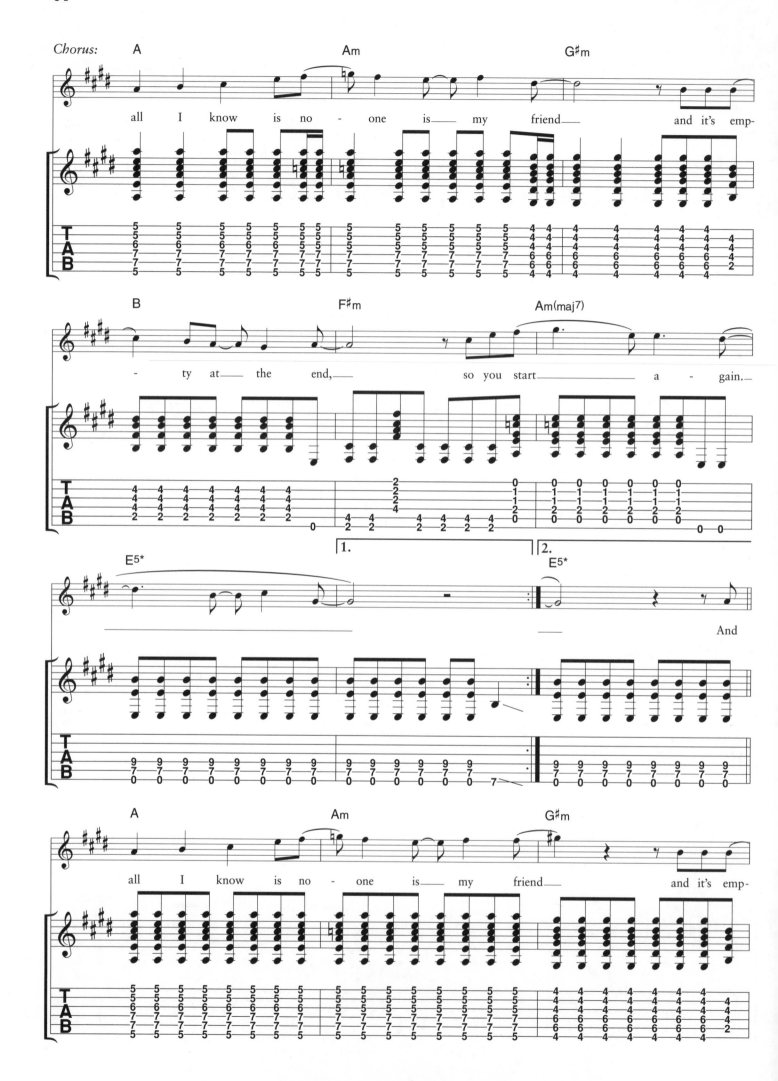

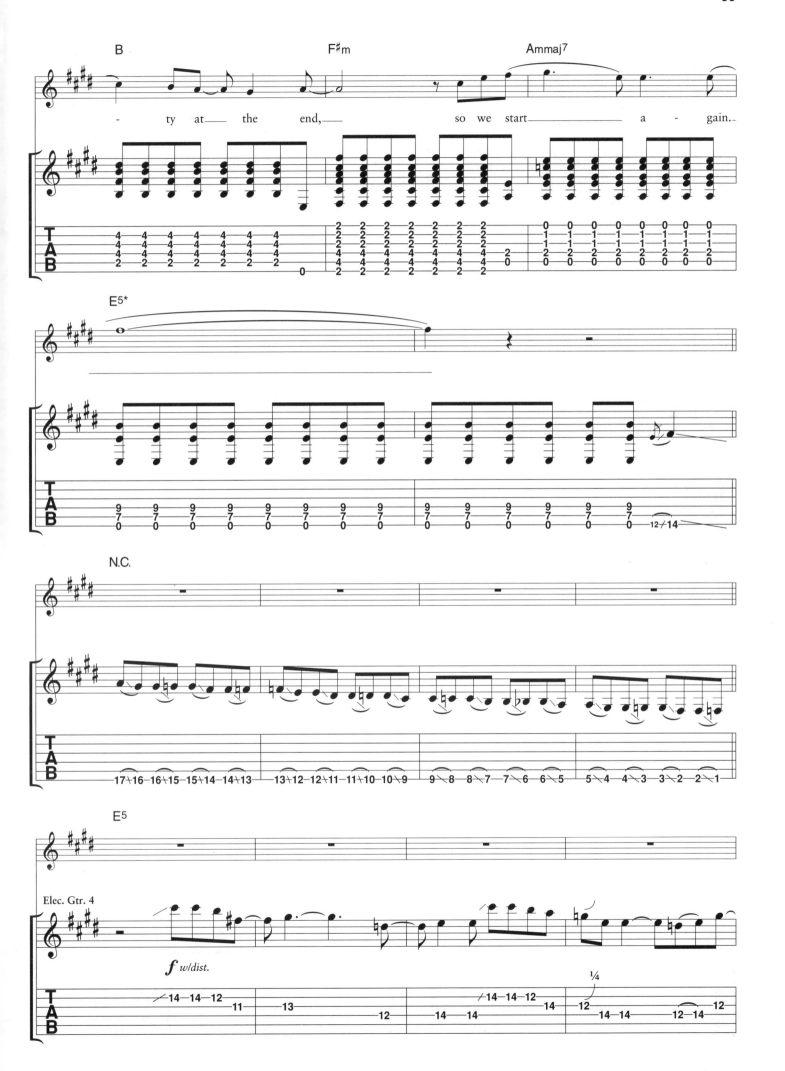

56

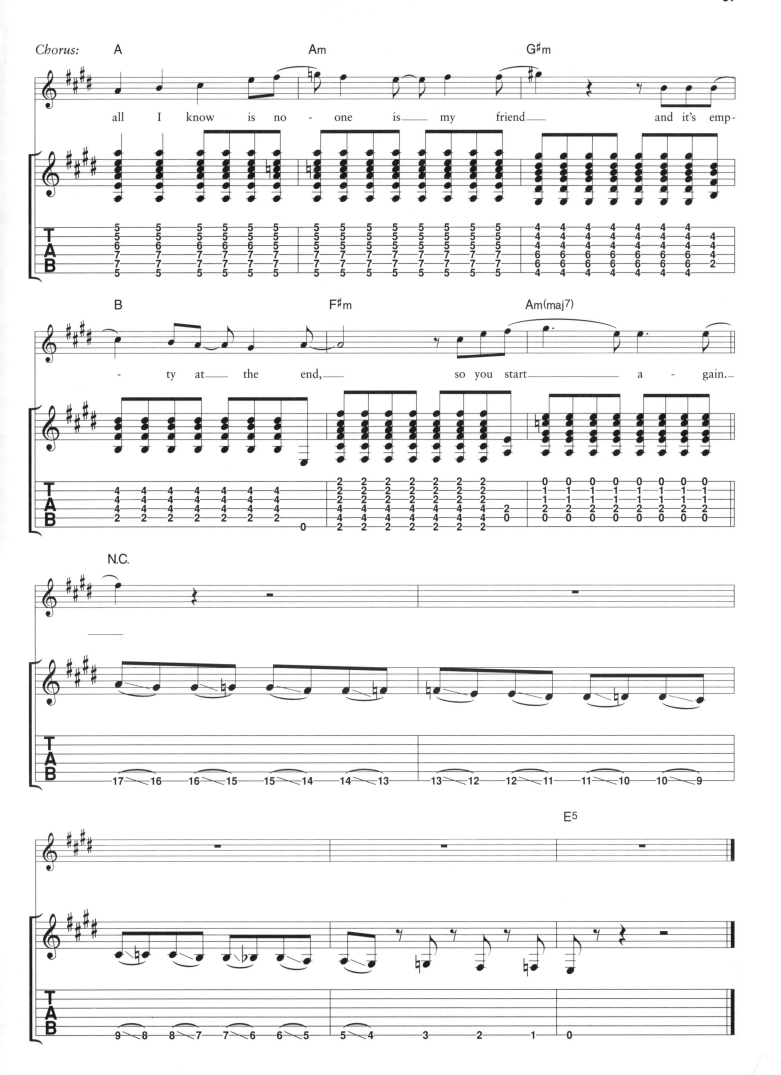

Fat Lip

Words and Music by Greig Nori, Deryck Whibley, Steve Jocz and Dave Baksh

* w/ delay repeats.

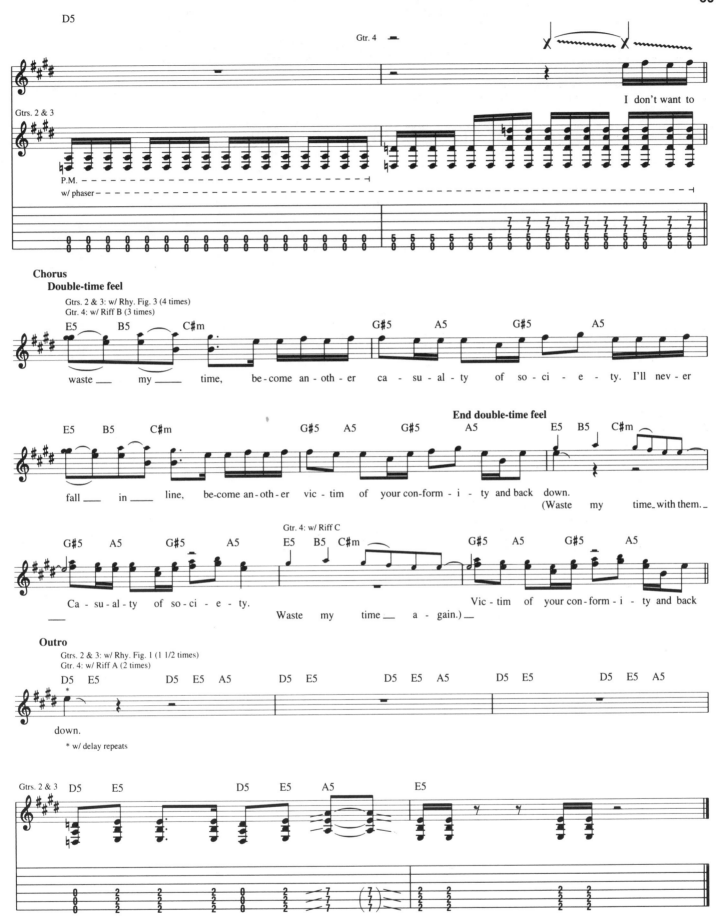

Additional Lyrics

2. Because you don't
   Know us at all, we laugh when old people fall.
   But what would you expect with a conscience so small?
   Heavy Metal and mullets, it's how we were raised.
   Maiden and Priest were the gods that we praised.

2nd Pre-Chorus:
'Cause we like having fun at other people's expense and
Cutting people down is just a minor offense then.
It's none of your concern, I guess I'll never learn.
I'm sick of being told to wait my turn.
I don't want to...

Fell In Love With A Girl

Words and Music by Jack White

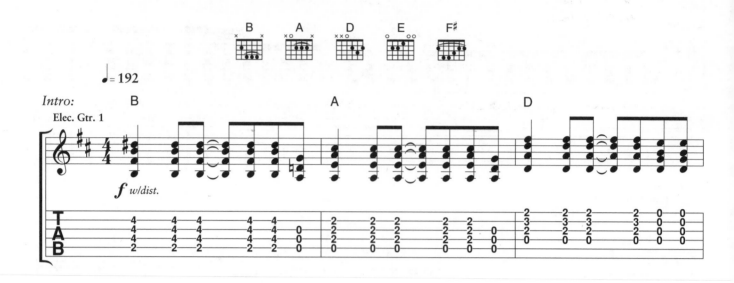

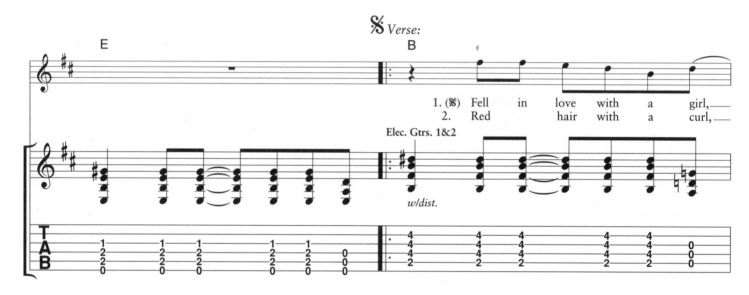

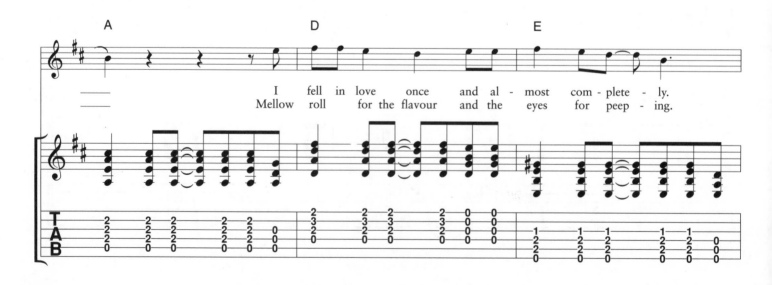

w/echo

Verse: (E)

3. House of—— jea-lous lov-ers, one hand con-tains the oth-er.

House of—— jea-lous lov-ers, a jea-lous lov-er's house.——————

Bass arr. for Gtr.

Solo: (E)

How You Remind Me

Words and Music by Chad Kroeger, Michael Kroeger, Ryan Peake and Ryan Vikedal

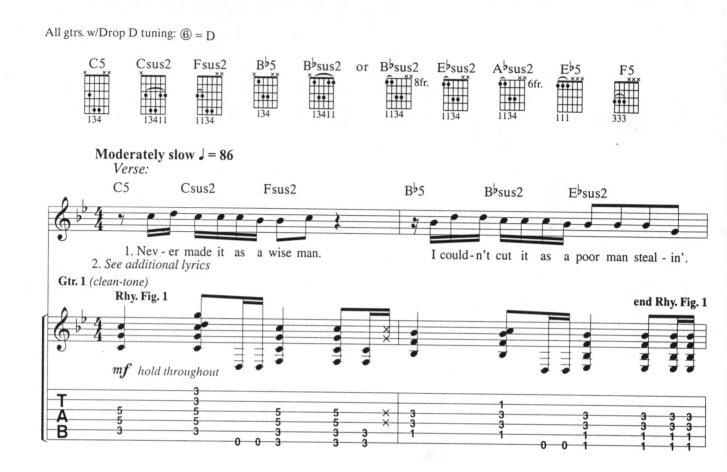

Chorus:

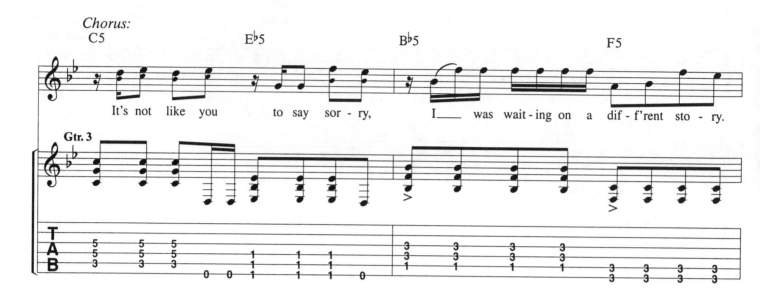

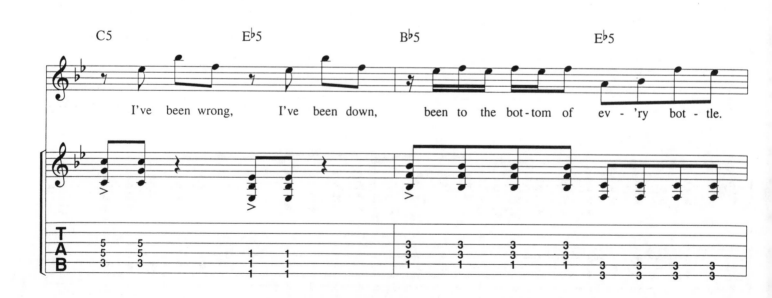

Verse 2:
It's not like you didn't know that.
I said I love you and I swear I still do.
And it must have been so bad.
'Cause livin' with me must have damn near killed you.

This is how you remind me of what I really am.
This is how you remind me of what I really am.
(To Chorus:)

A Minha Menina

Words and Music by Jorge Ben

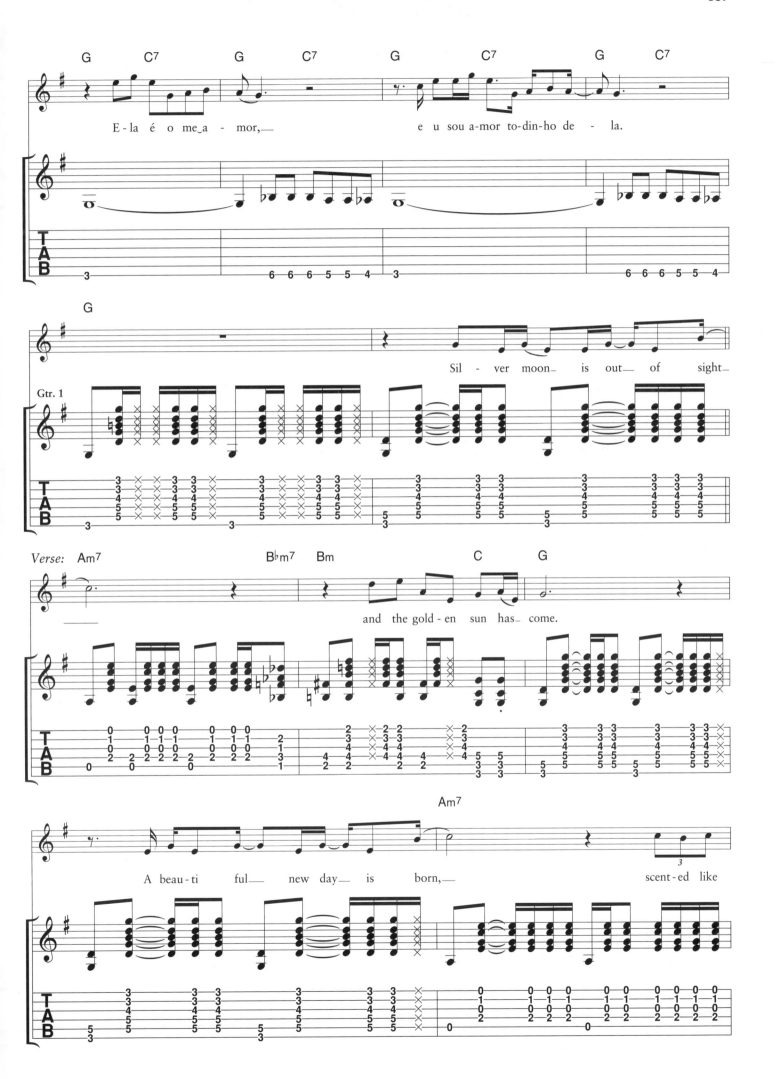

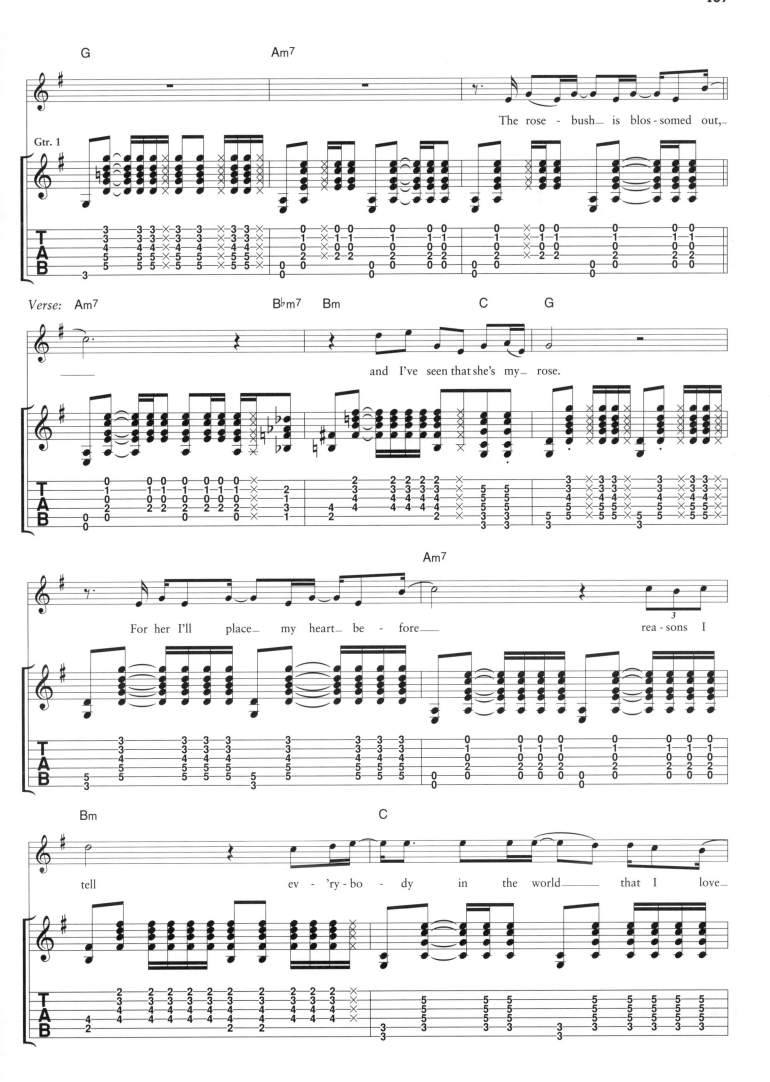

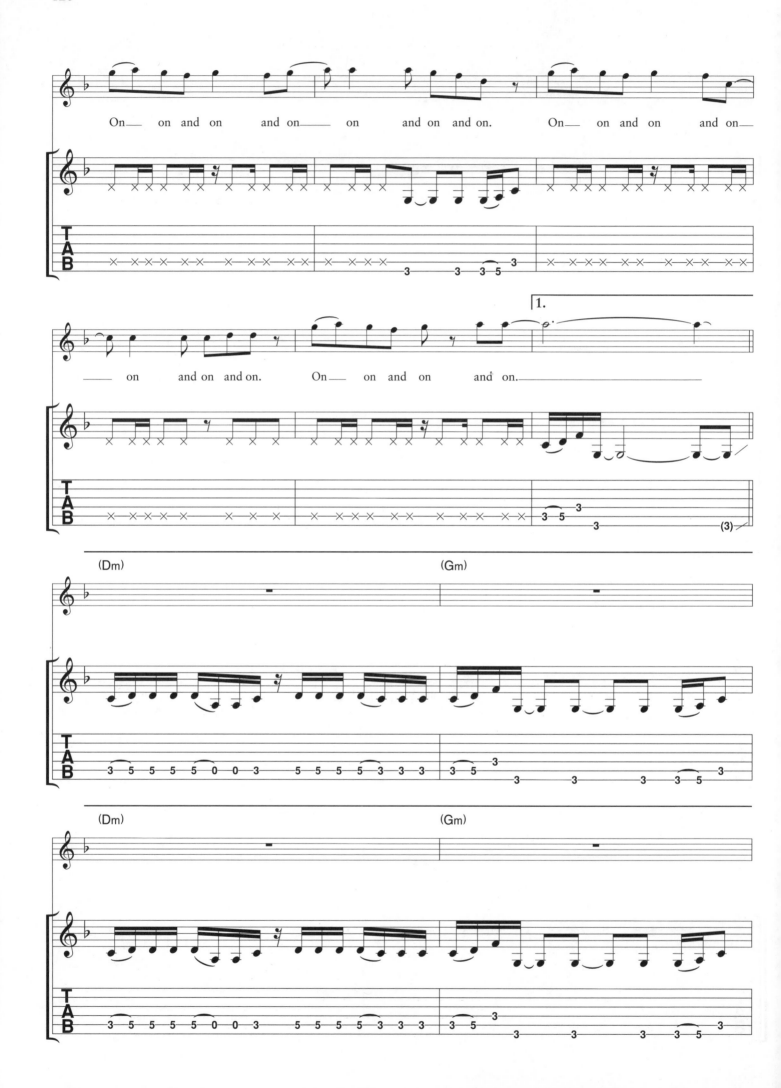

128

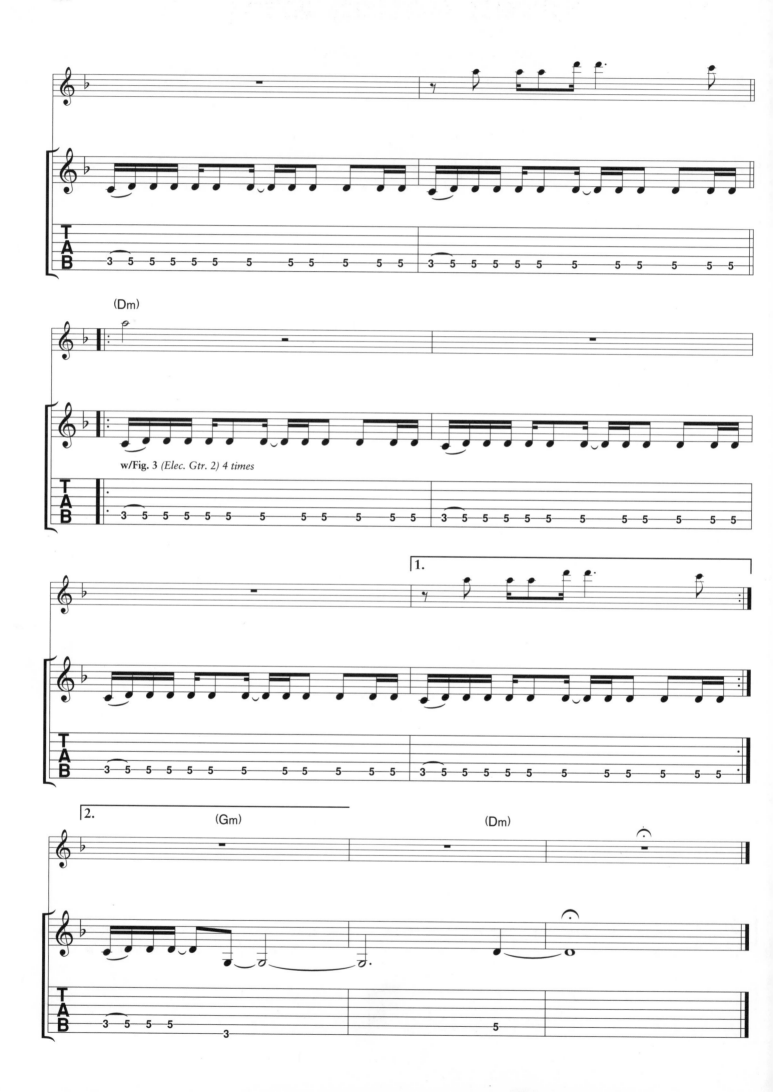

(Dm)

w/Fig. 3 *(Elec. Gtr. 2) 4 times*

1.

2.   (Gm)   (Dm)

Seven Nation Army

Words and Music by Jack White

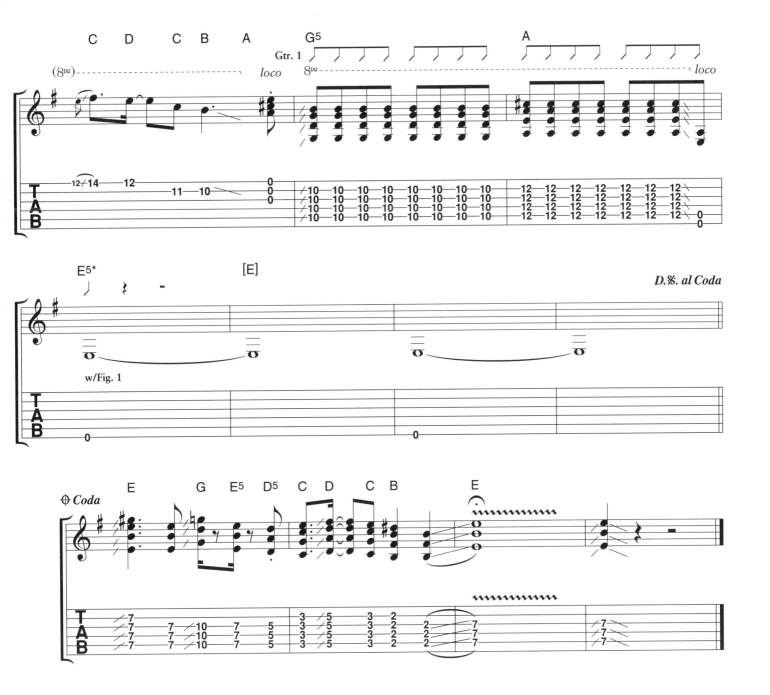

Verse 3:
I'm goin' to Wichita
Far from this opera for ever more
I'm gonna work the straw
Make the sweat drip out of every pore
And I'm bleedin' and I'm bleedin'
And I'm bleedin' right before the Lord
All the words are gonna bleed from me
And I will think no more
And the stains coming from my blood
Tells me go back home.

Remember Me

Words and Music by Martin Noble, Jan Wilkinson, Neil Wilkinson and Matthew Wood

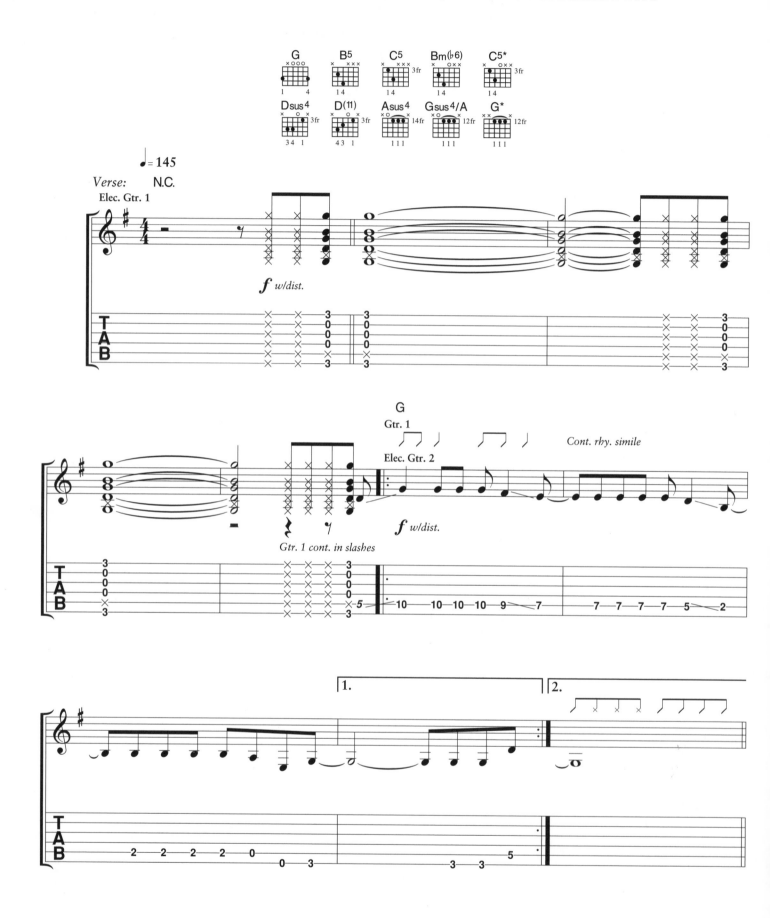

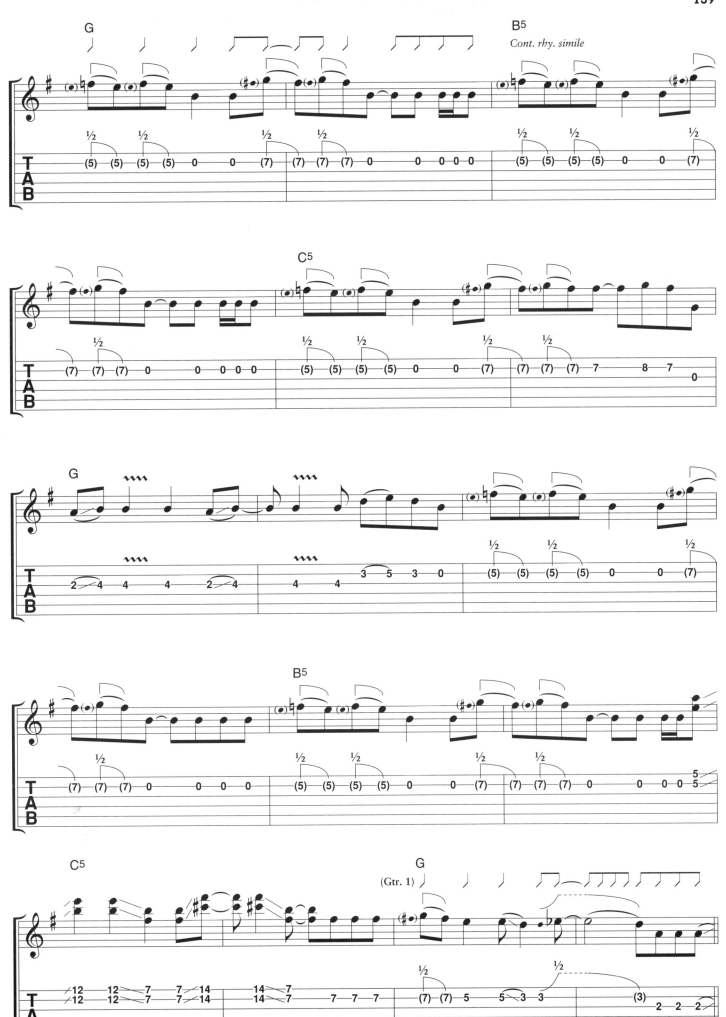

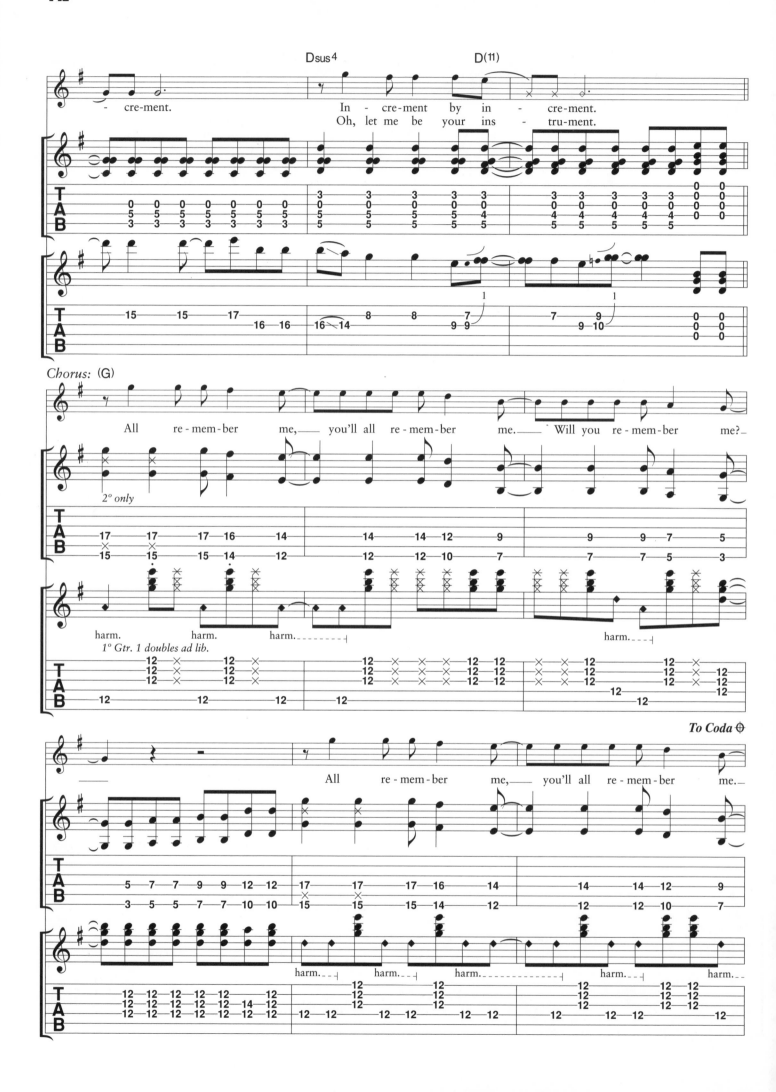

Will you re-mem-ber me?

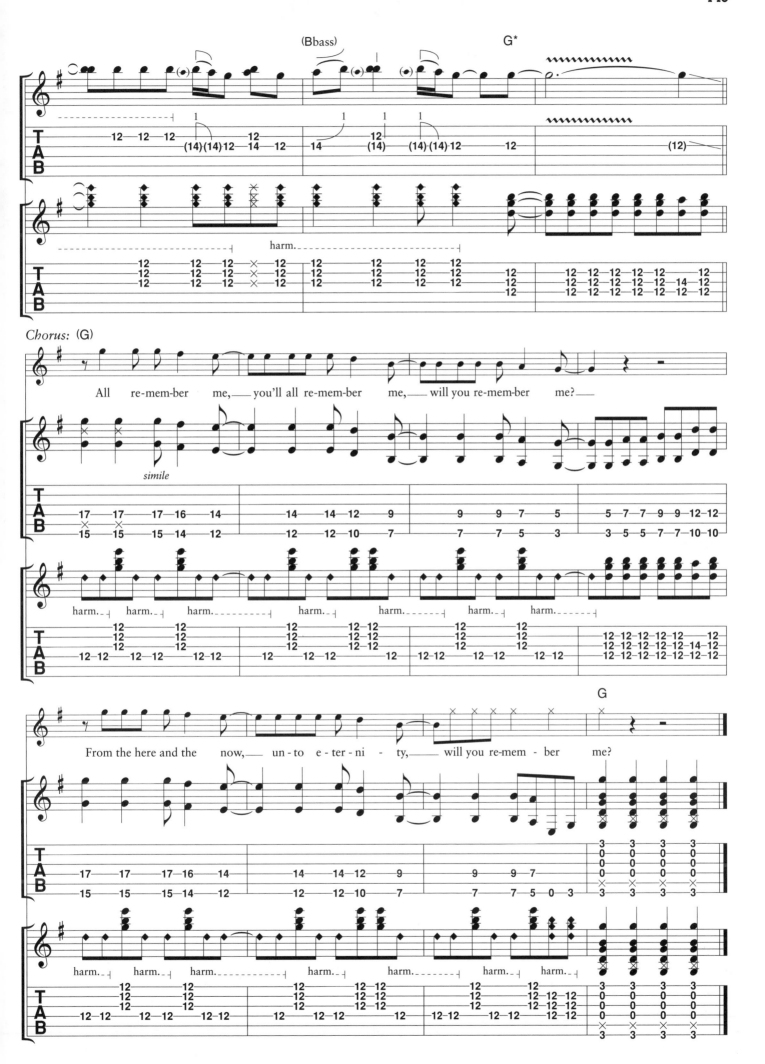

Rollover DJ

Words and Music by Nicholas Cester and Cameron Muncey

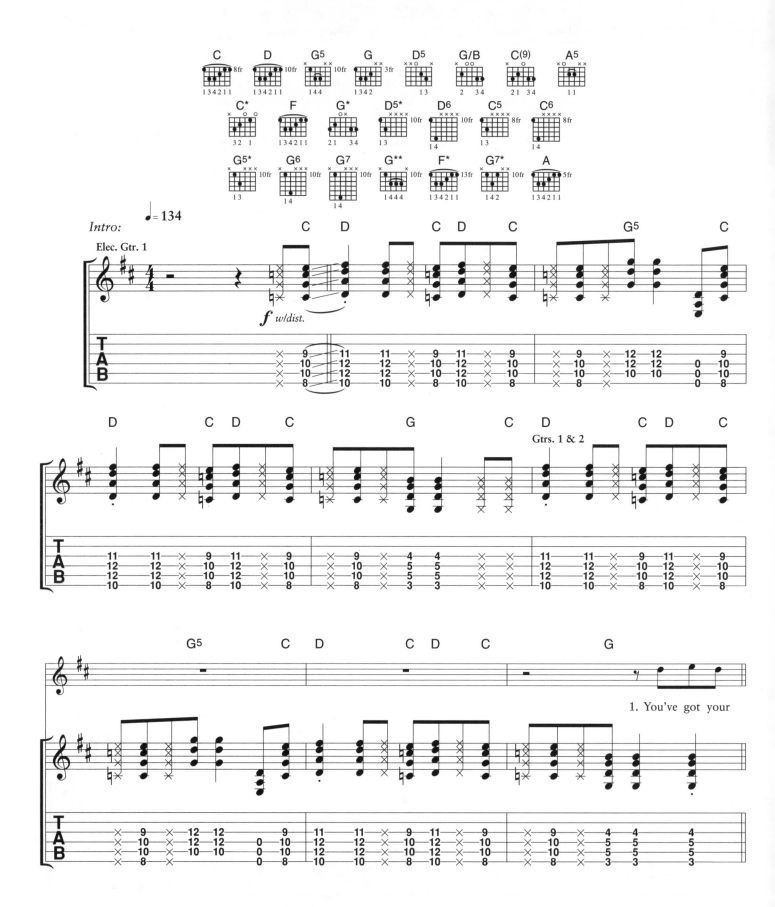

1. You've got your

Hey! Roll-ov-er D. J.___ if you don't___ mind.___

There Goes The Fear

Words and Music by Jimi Goodwin, Jez Williams and Andy Williams

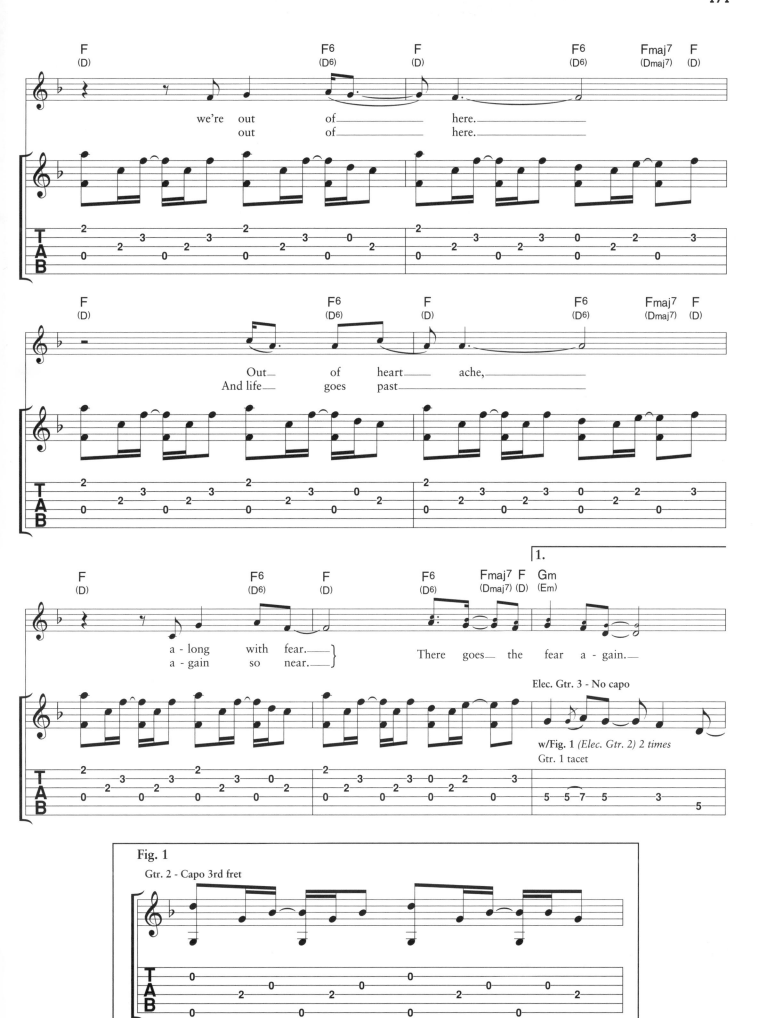

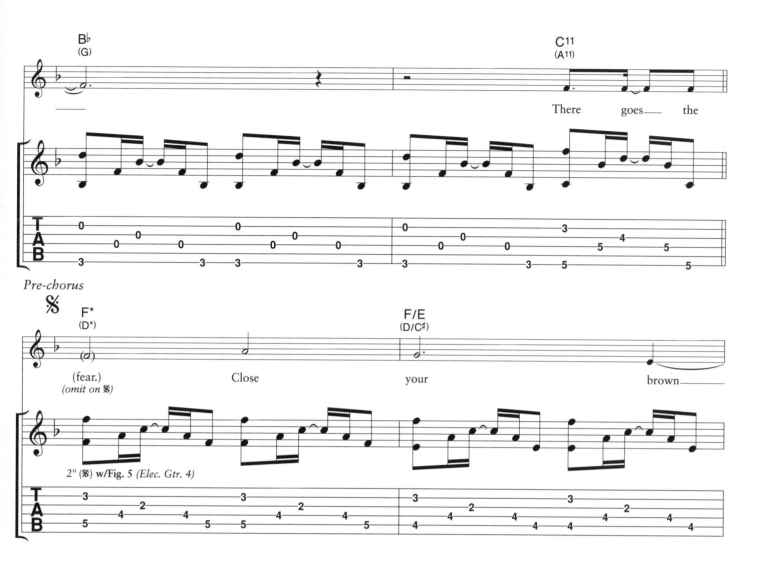

Pre-chorus

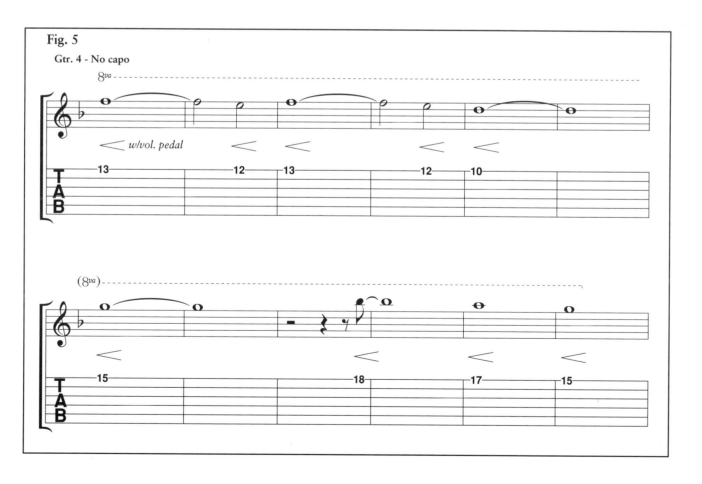

Fig. 5

Gtr. 4 - No capo

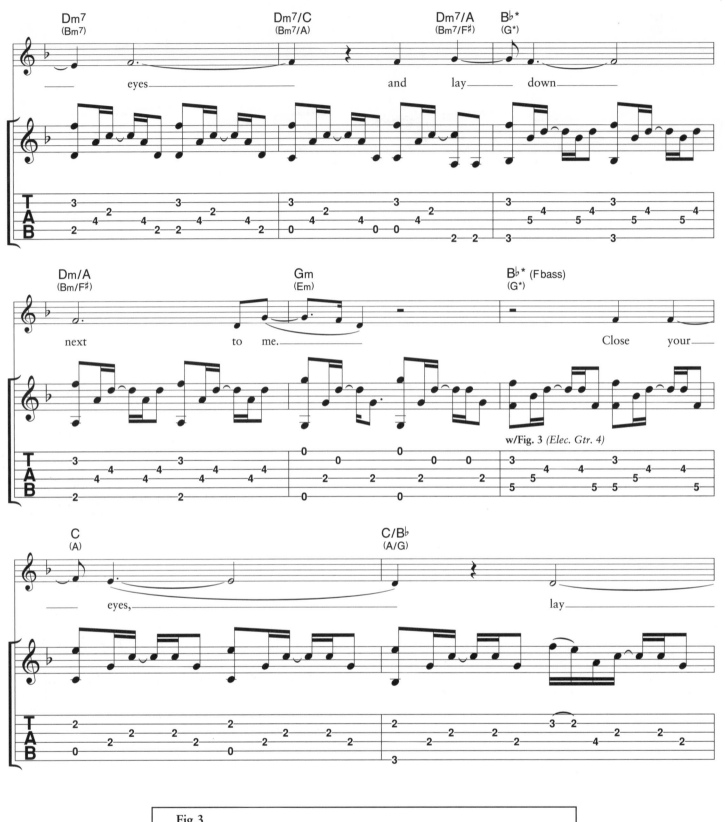

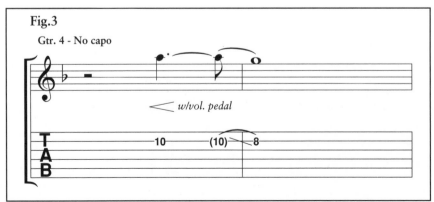

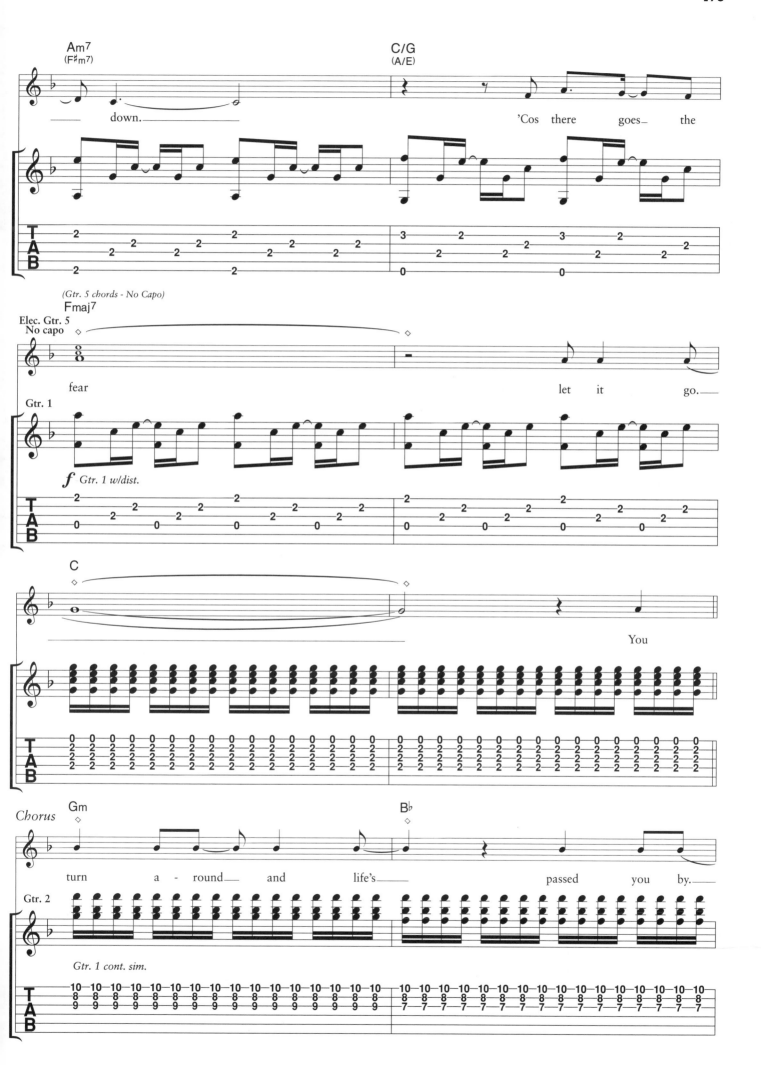

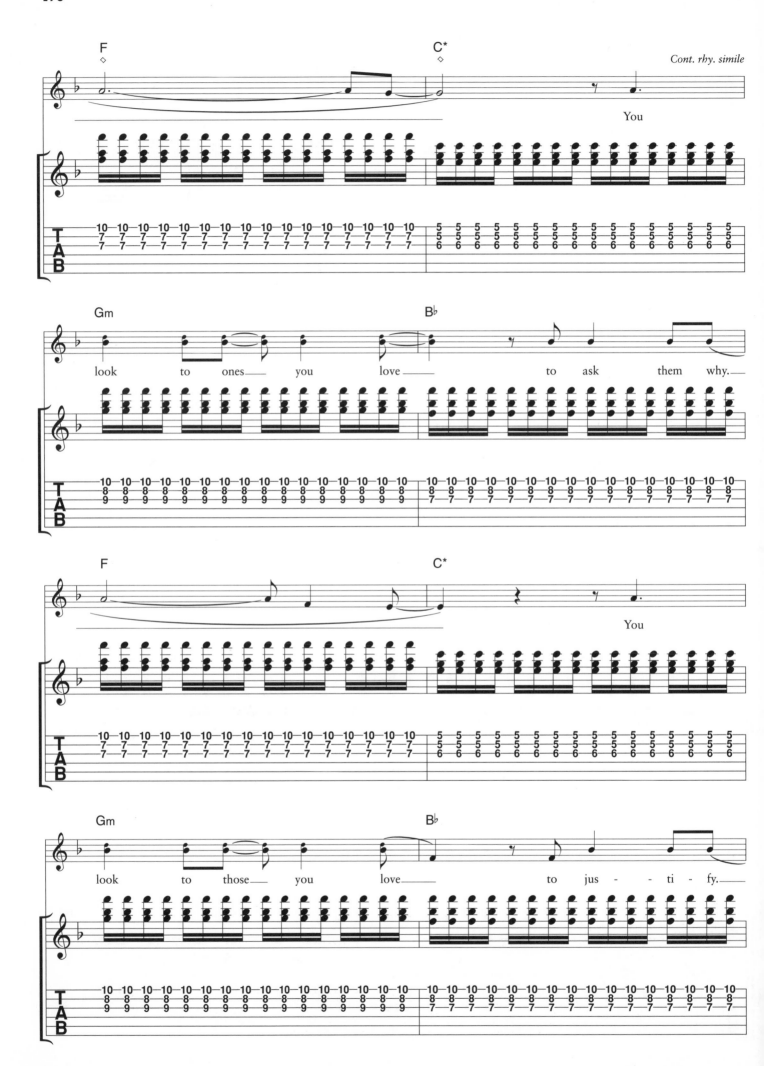

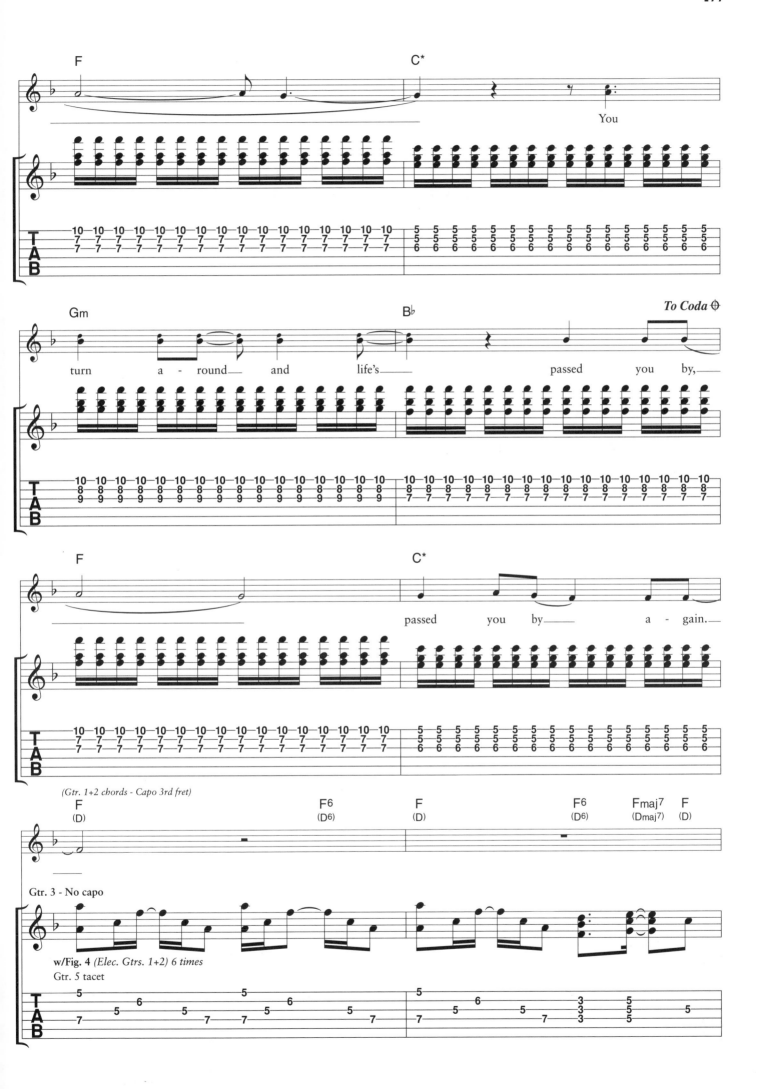

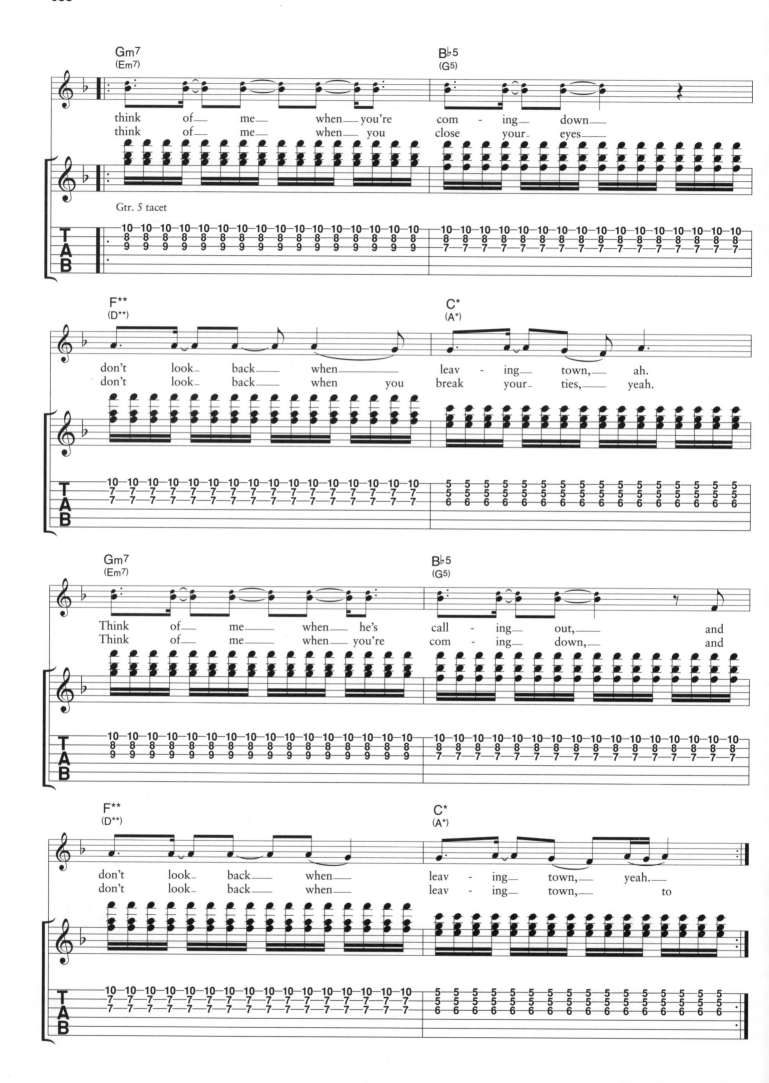

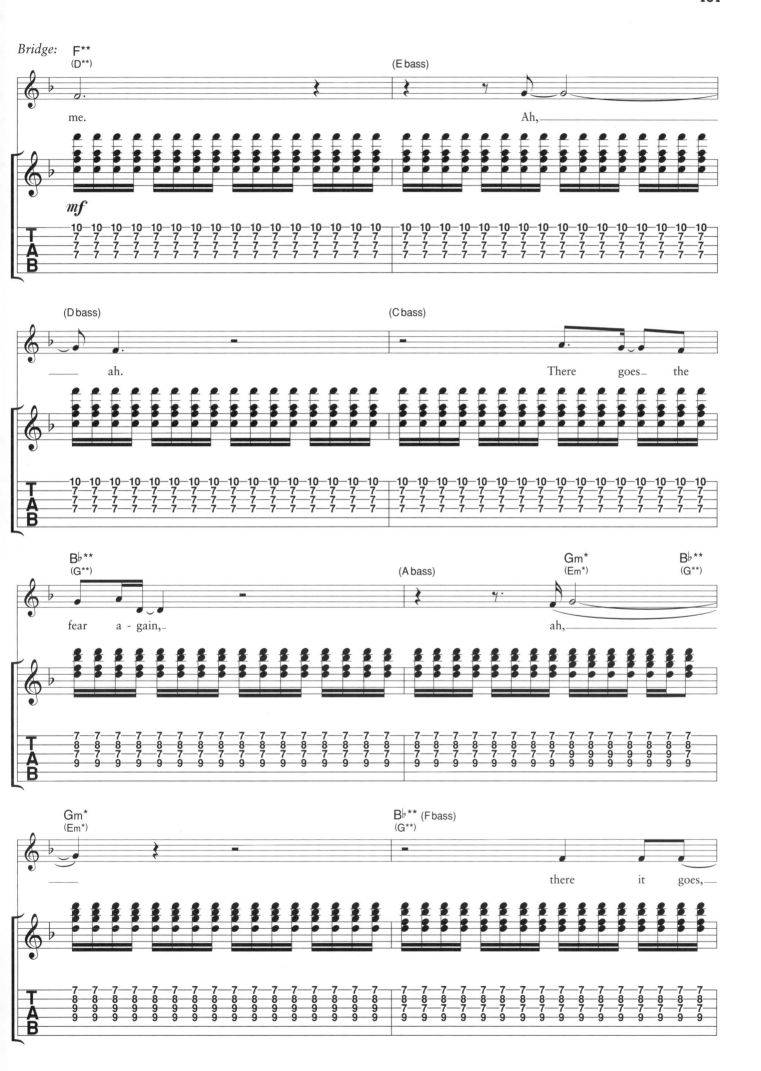

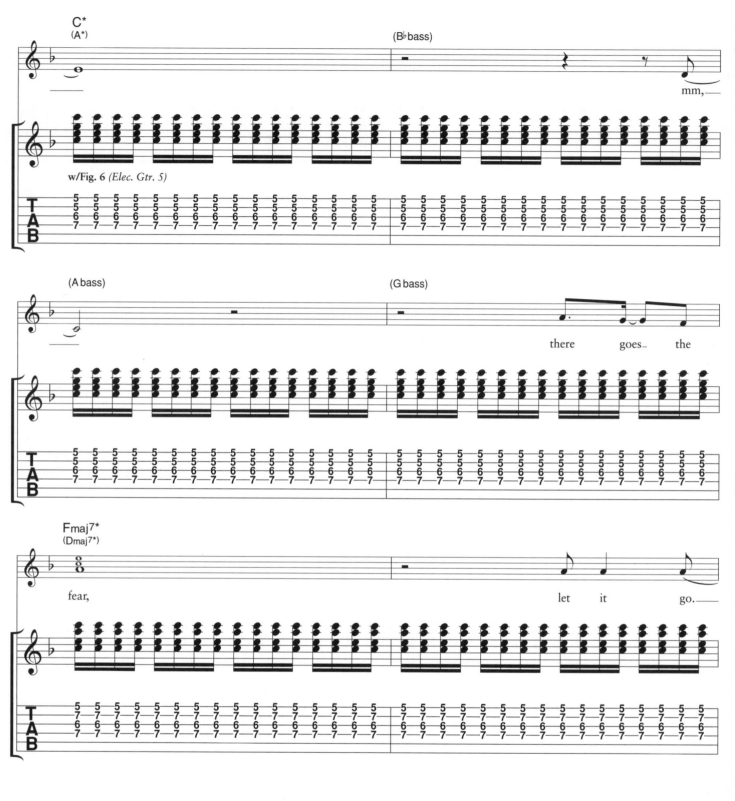

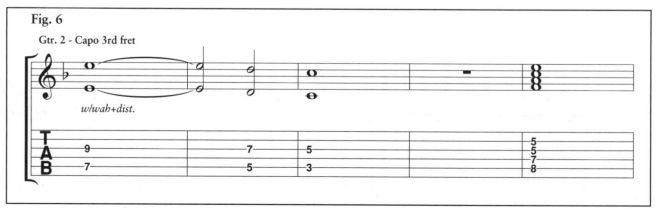

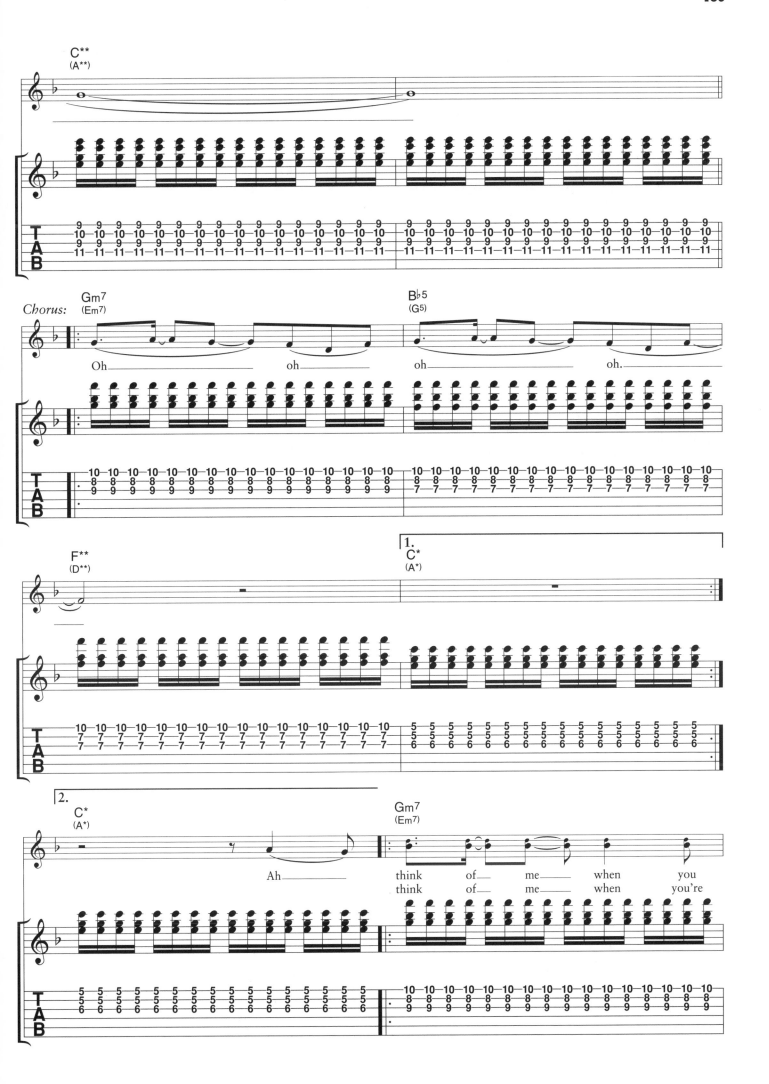

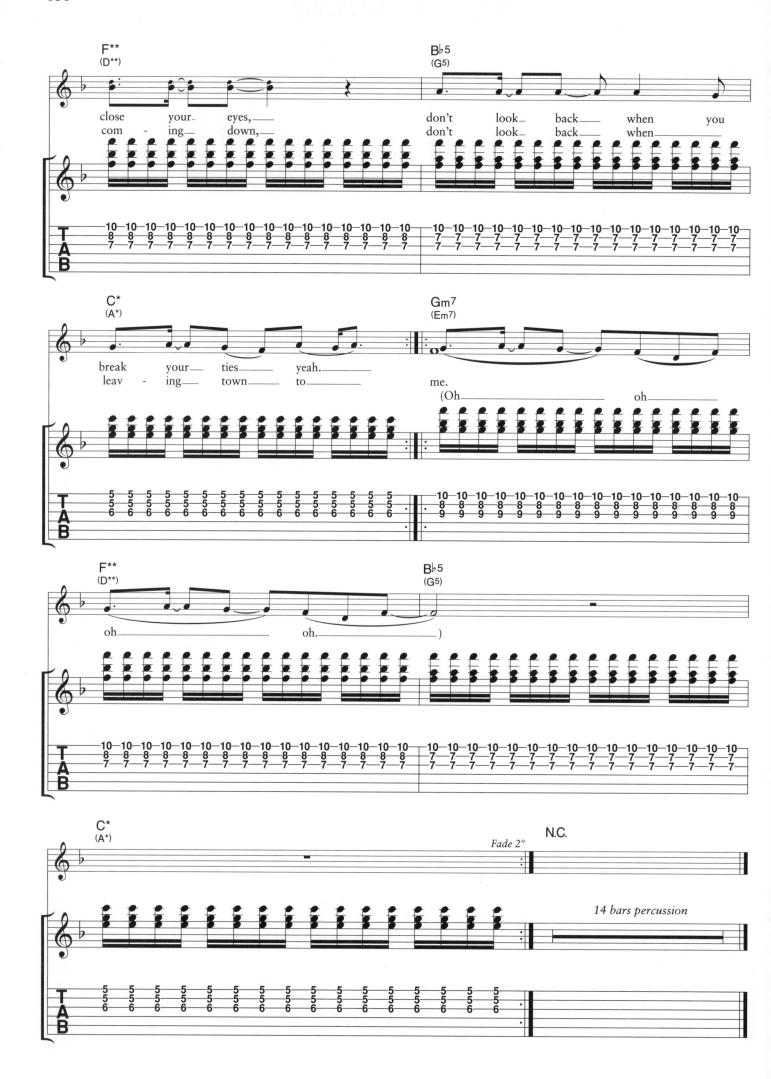

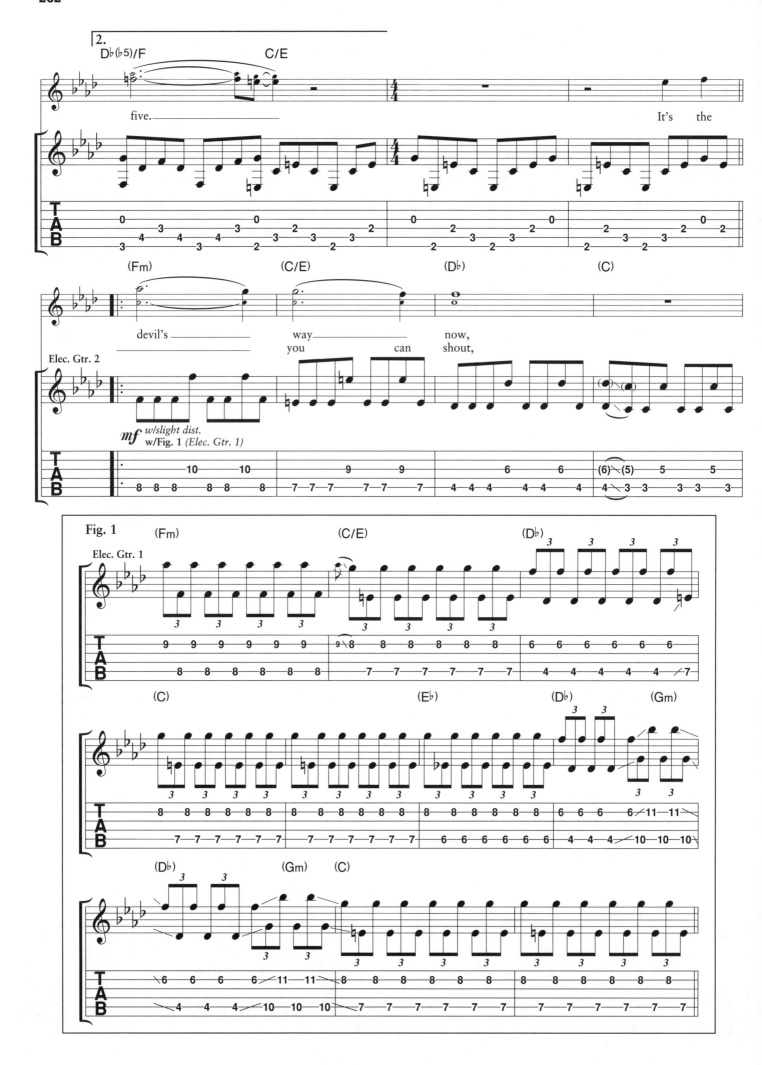

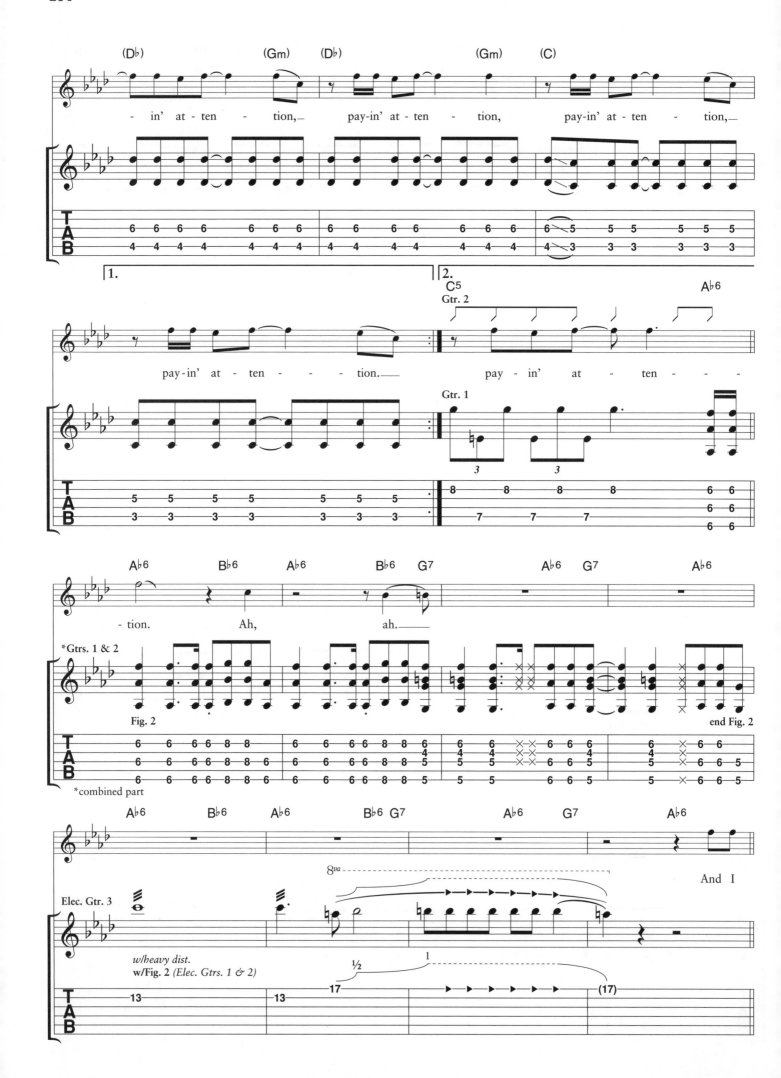

We're All In Love

Words and Music by Peter Hayes, Robert Been and Nicholas Jago

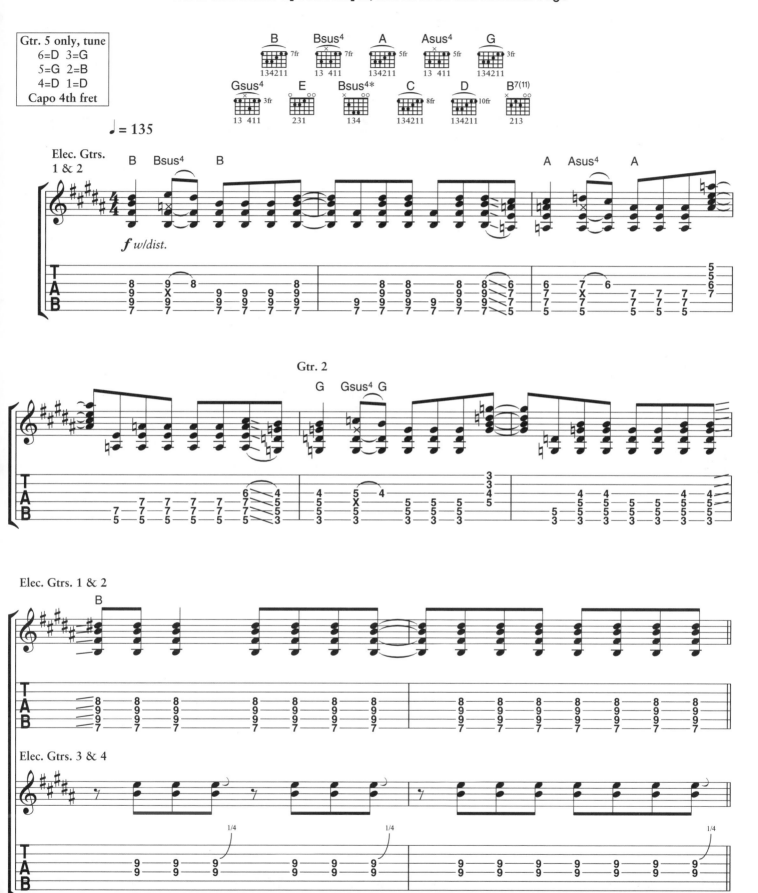

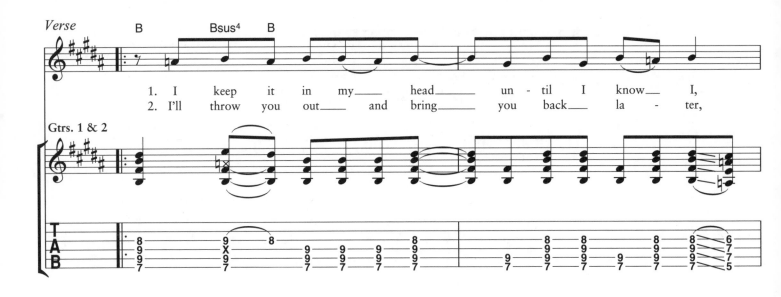

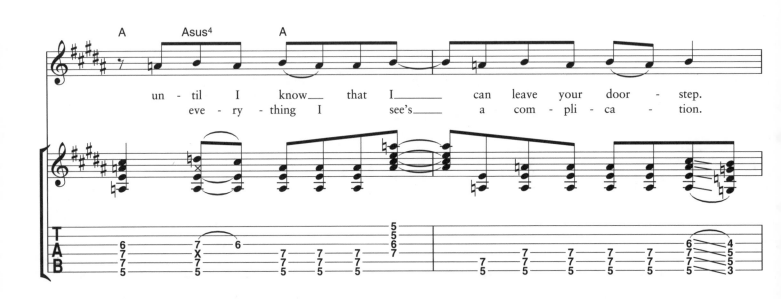

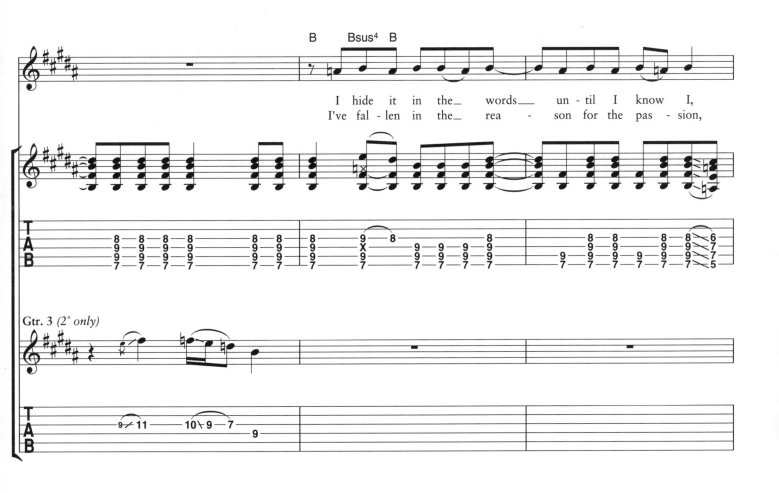

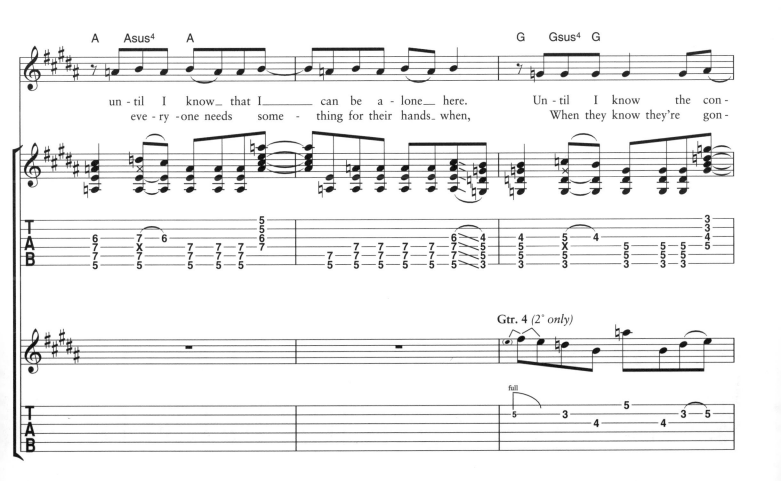

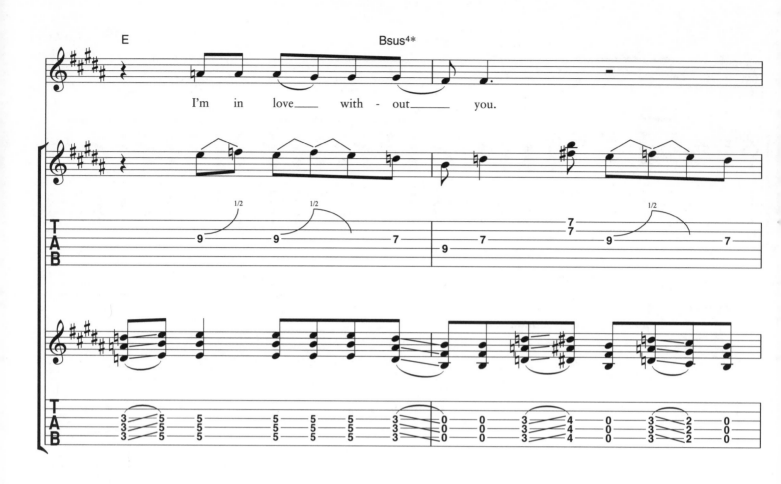

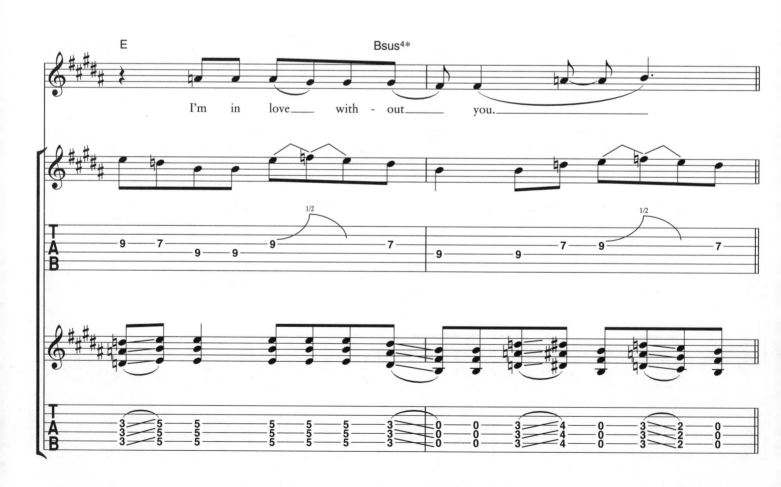

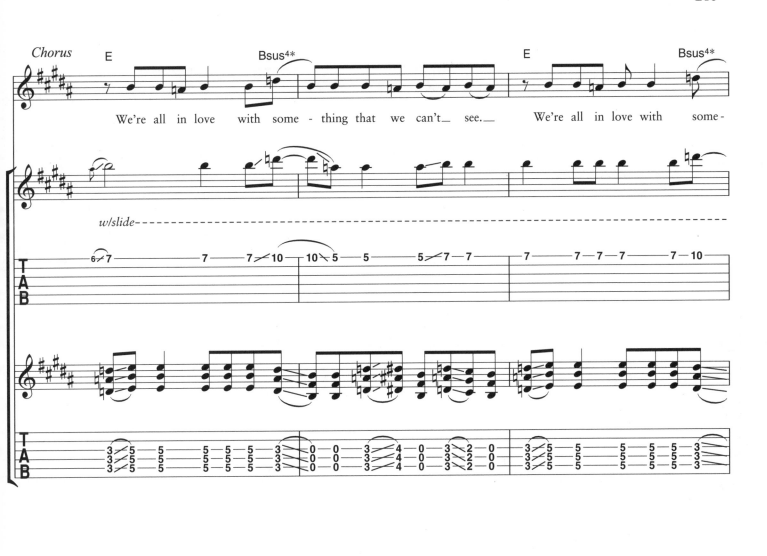

Chorus

We're all in love with some-thing that we can't see. We're all in love with some-

-thing that we can't see. I'm in love with some-thing that I can't see.

The Young & The Hopeless

Words and Music by Benjamin Combs and Joel Combs

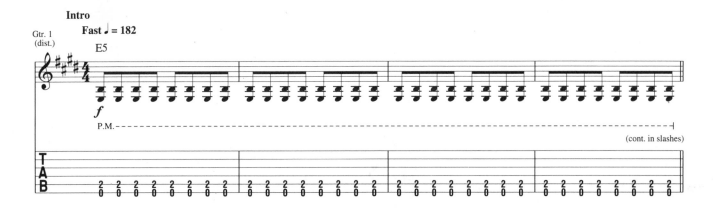

Tune down 1/2 step:
(low to high) Eb-Ab-Db-Gb-Bb-Eb

Intro

Gtr. 1
(dist.)

Fast ♩ = 182

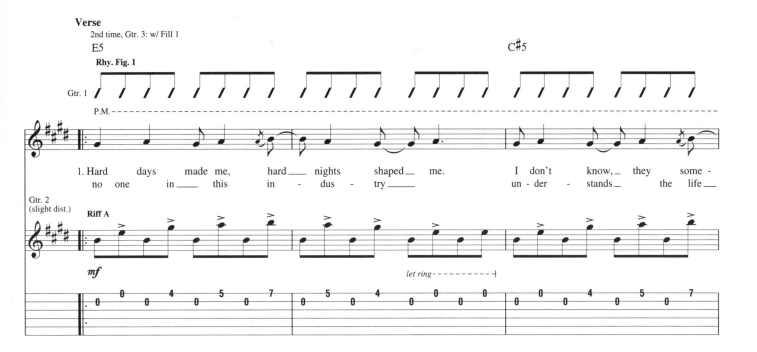

Verse

2nd time, Gtr. 3: w/ Fill 1

Gtr. 1

Rhy. Fig. 1

P.M.

1. Hard days made me, hard nights shaped me. I don't know, they some-
no one in this in-dus-try un-der-stands the life

Gtr. 2
(slight dist.)

Riff A

mf

let ring

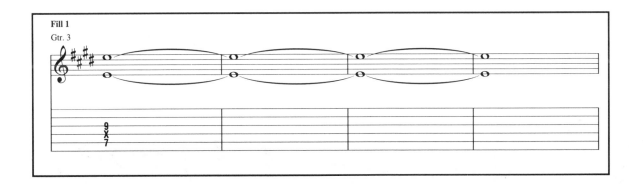

Fill 1

Gtr. 3

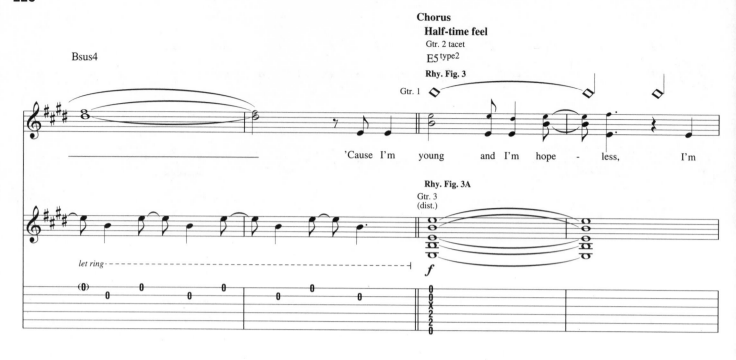

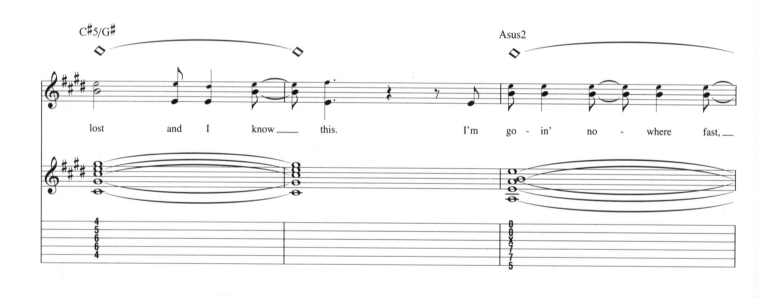

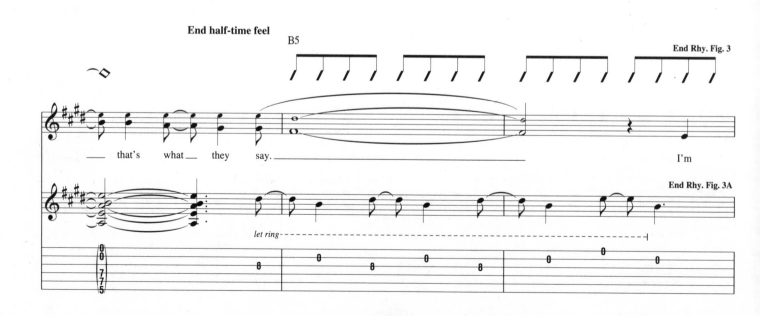

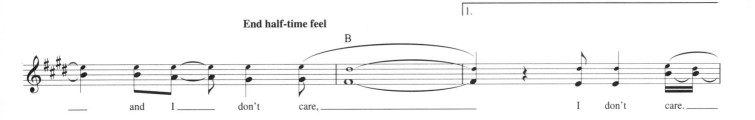
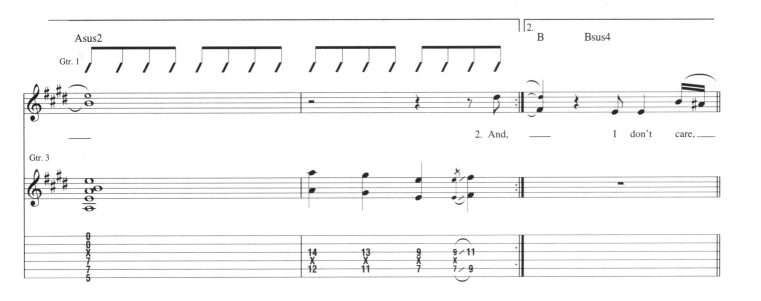
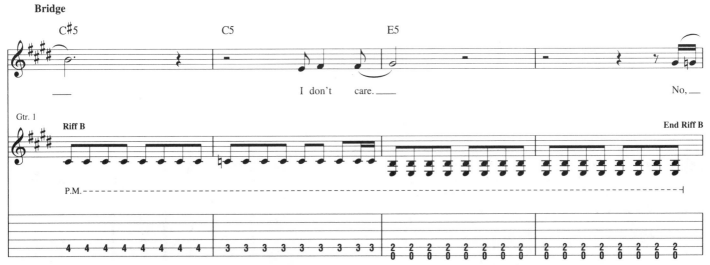

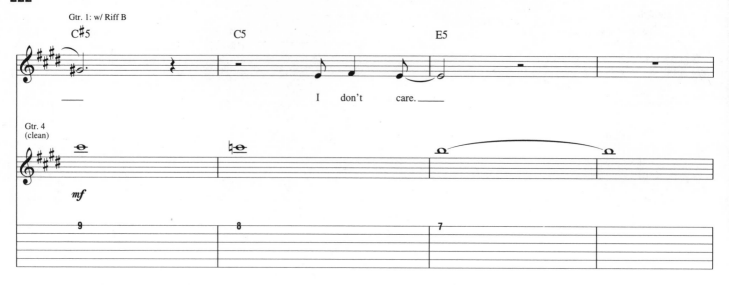

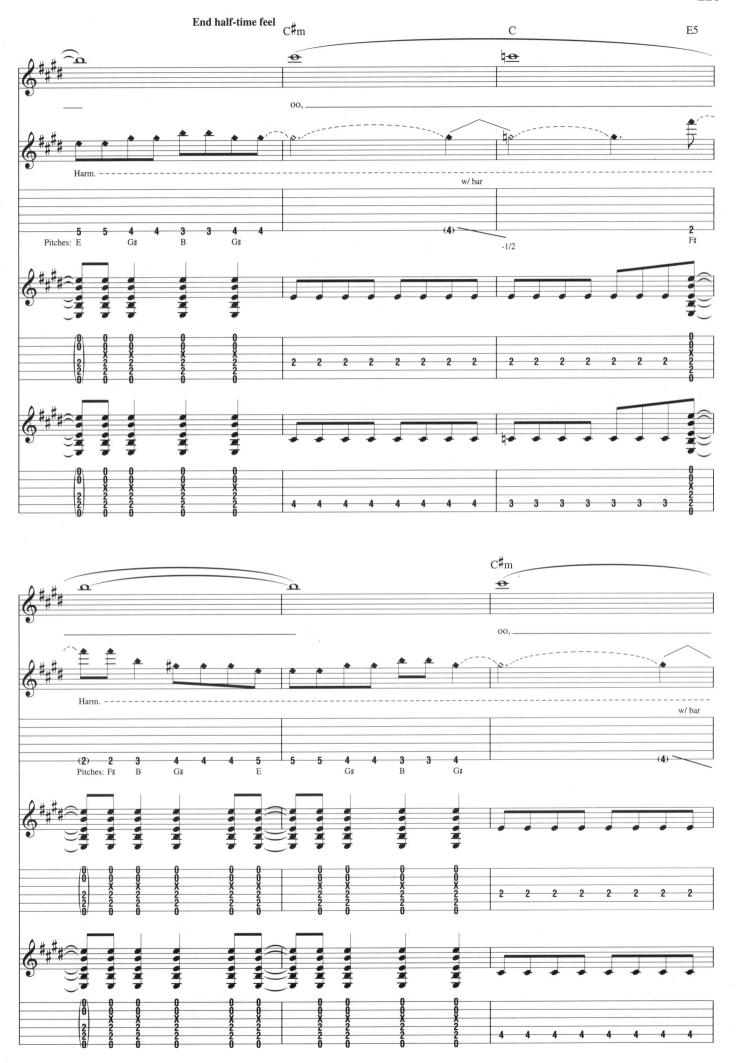

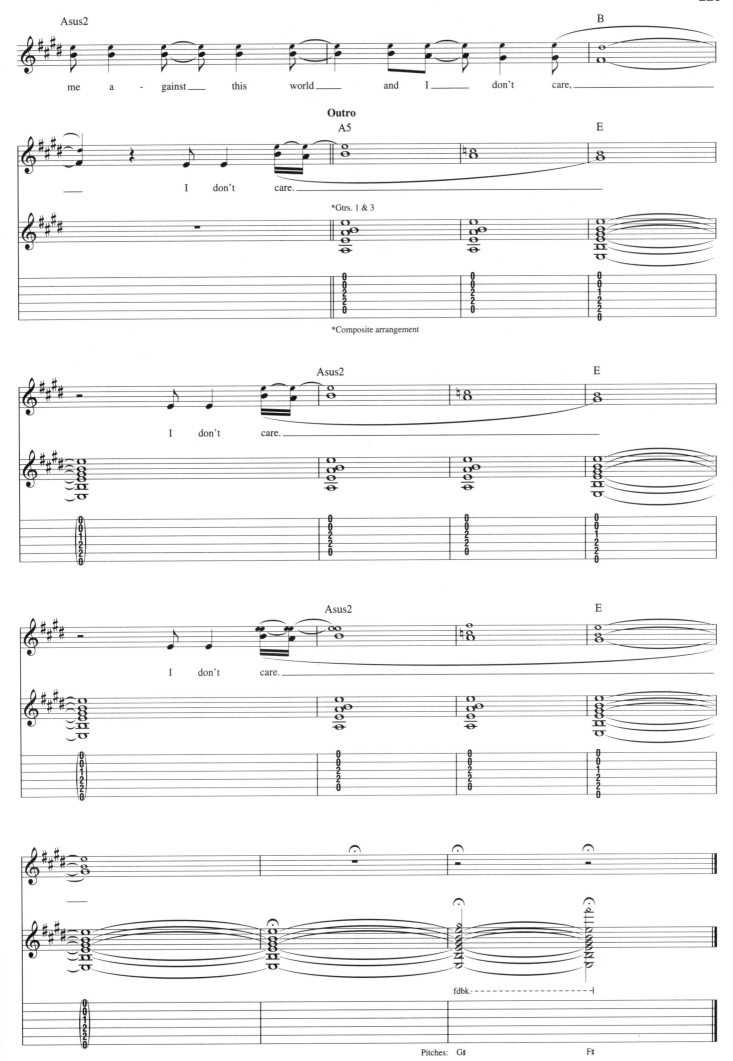

GUITAR TAB GLOSSARY**

TABLATURE EXPLANATION

READING TABLATURE: Tablature illustrates the six strings of the guitar. Notes and chords are indicated by the placement of fret numbers on a given string(s).

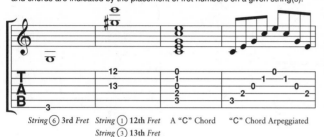

String ⑥ **3rd** *Fret*   *String* ① **12th** *Fret*   A "C" Chord   "C" Chord Arpeggiated
String ③ **13th** *Fret*

BENDING NOTES

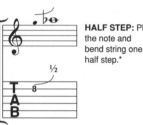

HALF STEP: Play the note and bend string one half step.*

PREBEND (Ghost Bend): Bend to the specified note, before the string is picked.

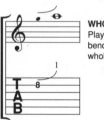

WHOLE STEP: Play the note and bend string one whole step.

PREBEND AND RELEASE: Bend the string, play it, then release to the original note.

WHOLE STEP AND A HALF: Play the note and bend string a whole step and a half.

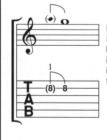

REVERSE BEND: Play the already-bent string, then immediately drop it down to the fretted note.

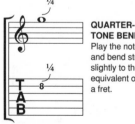

QUARTER-TONE BEND: Play the note and bend string slightly to the equivalent of half a fret.

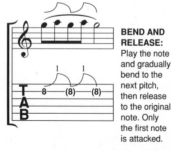

BEND AND RELEASE: Play the note and gradually bend to the next pitch, then release to the original note. Only the first note is attacked.

*A half step is the smallest interval in Western music; it is equal to one fret. A whole step equals two frets.

UNISON BEND: Play both notes and immediately bend the lower note to the same pitch as the higher note.

DOUBLE NOTE BEND: Play both notes and immediately bend both strings simultaneously.

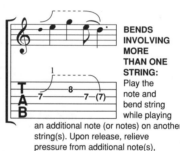

BENDS INVOLVING MORE THAN ONE STRING: Play the note and bend string while playing an additional note (or notes) on another string(s). Upon release, relieve pressure from additional note(s), causing original note to sound alone.

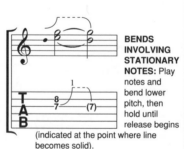

BENDS INVOLVING STATIONARY NOTES: Play notes and bend lower pitch, then hold until release begins (indicated at the point where line becomes solid).

TREMOLO BAR

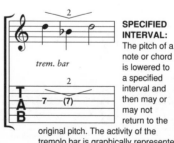

SPECIFIED INTERVAL: The pitch of a note or chord is lowered to a specified interval and then may or may not return to the original pitch. The activity of the tremolo bar is graphically represented by peaks and valleys.

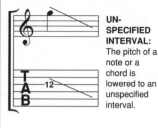

UNSPECIFIED INTERVAL: The pitch of a note or a chord is lowered to an unspecified interval.

HARMONICS

NATURAL HARMONIC: A finger of the fret hand lightly touches the note or notes indicated in the tab and is played by the pick hand.

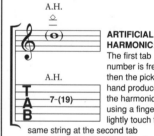

ARTIFICIAL HARMONIC: The first tab number is fretted, then the pick hand produces the harmonic by using a finger to lightly touch the same string at the second tab number (in parenthesis) and is then picked by another finger.

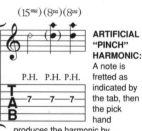

ARTIFICIAL "PINCH" HARMONIC: A note is fretted as indicated by the tab, then the pick hand produces the harmonic by squeezing the pick firmly while using the tip of the index finger in the pick attack. If parenthesis are found around the fretted note, it does not sound. No parenthesis means both the fretted note and A.H. are heard simultaneously.

**By Kenn Chipkin and Aaron Stang

RHYTHM SLASHES

STRUM INDICATIONS: Strum with indicated rhythm.

The chord voicings are found on the first page of the transcription underneath the song title.

SINGLE NOTES IN SLASH NOTATION: A regular notehead indicates a single note. The circled number below the note indicates which string of the chord to strike. If the note is not in the chord, the fret number will be indicated above the note(s).

ARTICULATIONS

HAMMER ON: Play lower note, then "hammer on" to higher note with another finger. Only the first note is attacked.

LEFT HAND HAMMER: Hammer on the first note played on each string with the left hand.

PULL OFF: Play higher note, then "pull off" to lower note with another finger. Only the first note is attacked.

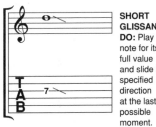

FRET-BOARD TAPPING: "Tap" onto the note indicated by + with a finger of the pick hand, then pull off to the following note held by the fret hand.

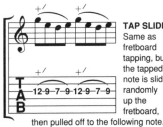

TAP SLIDE: Same as fretboard tapping, but the tapped note is slid randomly up the fretboard, then pulled off to the following note.

BEND AND TAP TECHNIQUE: Play note and bend to specified interval. While holding bend, tap onto note indicated.

LEGATO SLIDE: Play note and slide to the following note. (Only first note is attacked).

LONG GLISSAN-DO: Play note and slide in specified direction for the full value of the note.

SHORT GLISSAN-DO: Play note for its full value and slide in specified direction at the last possible moment.

PICK SLIDE: Slide the edge of the pick in specified direction across the length of the string(s).

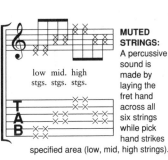

low mid. high stgs. stgs. stgs.

MUTED STRINGS: A percussive sound is made by laying the fret hand across all six strings while pick hand strikes specified area (low, mid, high strings).

PALM MUTE: The note or notes are muted by the palm of the pick hand by lightly touching the string(s) near the bridge.

trem. pick

TREMOLO PICKING: The note or notes are picked as fast as possible.

TRILL: Hammer on and pull off consecutively and as fast as possible between the original note and the grace note.

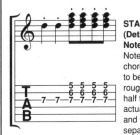

ACCENT: Notes or chords are to be played with added emphasis.

STACCATO (Detached Notes): Notes or chords are to be played roughly half their actual value and with separation.

DOWN STROKES AND UPSTROKES: Notes or chords are to be played with either a downstroke (■) or upstroke (∨) of the pick.

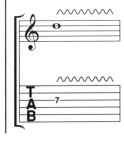

VIBRATO: The pitch of a note is varied by a rapid shaking of the fret hand finger, wrist, and forearm.

Songs guitars were meant to play

Essential Acoustic Playlist 2
9854A   VC   ISBN: 1-84328-411-1

A Minha Meninha (The Bees) – Ain't That Enough (Teenage Fanclub) – All Together Now (The Farm) – Alright (Supergrass) – Am I Wrong (Mull Historical Society) – American English (Idlewild) – Average Man (Turin Brakes) – Beetlebum (Blur) – Breakfast at Tiffany's (Deep Blue Something) – Buy It In Bottles (Richard Ashcroft) – Can You Dig It? (The Mock Turtles) – Caught By The River (Doves) – Coffee & TV (Blur) – Come Away With Me (Norah Jones) – Come Back To What You Know (Embrace) – Common People (Pulp) – Crazy Beat (Blur) – Creep (Radiohead) – A Design For Life (Manic Street Preachers) – Distant Sun (Crowded House) – Don't Let Me Down Gently (The Wonderstuff) – Don't Think You're The First (The Coral) – Everlong (Foo Fighters) – Fallen Angel (Elbow) – Fastboy (The Bluetones) – The Final Arrears (Mull Historical Society) – Forget About Tomorrow (Feeder) – Getting Away With It (Electronic) – Go To Sleep (Radiohead) – Grace (Supergrass) – Here's Where The Story Ends (The Sundays) – High And Dry (Radiohead) – History (The Verve) – Hooligan (Embrace) – I Need Direction (Teenage Fanclub) – I Will (Radiohead) – (I'm Gonna) Cry Myself Blind (Primal Scream) – In A Room (Dodgy) – It's True That We Love One Another (The White Stripes) – Just When You're Thinkin' Things Over (The Charlatans) – La Breeze (Simian) – Lilac Wine (Jeff Buckley) – A Little Like You (Grand Drive) – Live In A Hiding Place (Idlewild) – Lucky (Radiohead) – A Man Needs To Be Told (The Charlatans) – No Surprises (Radiohead) – Only Happy When It Rains (Garbage) – Out Of Time (Blur) – Painkiller (Turin Brakes) – Pass It On (The Coral) – Personal Jesus (Johnny Cash) – Pineapple Head (Crowded House) – Poor Misguided Fool (Starsailor) – Road Rage (Catatonia) – Seen The Light (Supergrass) – Seven Nation Army (The White Stripes) – Shine On (The House Of Love) – Silence Is Easy (Starsailor) – Sk8ter Boi (Avril Lavigne) – Stay Away From Me (The Star Spangles) – There There (Radiohead) – Thinking About Tomorrow (Beth Orton) – This Is How It Feels (Inspiral Carpets) – Wake Up Boo! (The Boo Radleys) – Words (Doves) – Yoshimi Battles The Pink Robots (Flaming Lips) – You're So Pretty – We're So Pretty (The Charlatans) – You've Got Her In Your Pocket (The White Stripes)

Essential Acoustic Playlist
9701A   VC   ISBN: 1-84328-207-0

All The Small Things (Blink 182) – All You Good Good People (Embrace) – Angie (The Rolling Stones) – Any Day Now (Elbow) – Bittersweet Symphony (The Verve) – Buddy (Lemonheads) – Burning Down The House (Talking Heads) – Central Reservation (Beth Orton) – Come Together (Primal Scream) – Cryin' (Aerosmith) – Don't Dream It's Over (Crowded House) – The Drugs Don't Work (The Verve) – Empty At The End (Electric Soft Parade) – Everybody Hurts (R.E.M.) – Everyday Is Like Sunday (Morrissey) – Fast Car (Tracey Chapman) – Fat Lip (Sum 41) – Fell In Love With A Girl (The White Stripes) – Fireworks (Embrace) – Fly Away (Lenny Kravitz) – Future Boy (Turin Brakes) – Going Places (Teenage Fanclub) – Good Riddance (Green Day) – Heaven Knows I'm Miserable Now (The Smiths) – Hotel California (The Eagles) – Hotel Yorba (The White Stripes) – Hunter (Dido) – It's A Shame About Ray (Lemonheads) – Karma Police (Radiohead) – Kiss Me (Sixpence None The Richer) – Losing My Religion (R.E.M.) – Love Burns (Black Rebel Motorcycle Club) – The Man Who Told Everything (Doves) – Mansize Rooster (Supergrass) – Mellow Doubt (Teenage Fanclub) – Movin' On Up (Primal Scream) – Moving (Supergrass) – Mr. Jones (Counting Crows) – Next Year (Foo Fighters) – Novocaine For The Soul (Eels) – Over The Rainbow (Eva Cassidy) – Panic (The Smiths) – Porcelain (Moby) – Pounding (Doves) – Powder Blue (Elbow) – Rhythm & Blues Alibi (Gomez) – Save Tonight (Eagle Eye Cherry) – Silent Sigh (Badly Drawn Boy) – Secret Smile (Semisonic) – Shot Shot (Gomez) – Silent To The Dark (Electric Soft Parade) – Slight Return (The Bluetones) – Soak Up The Sun (Sheryl Crow) – Something In My Eye (Ed Harcourt) – Something To Talk About (Badly Drawn Boy) – Song 2 (Blur) – Song For The Lovers (Richard Ashcroft) – Standing Still (Jewel) – Street Spirit (Fade Out) (Radiohead) – Teenage Dirtbag (Wheatus) – Tender (Blur) – There Goes The Fear (Doves) – Time In A Bottle (Jim Croce) – Underdog (Save Me) (Turin Brakes) – Walking After You (Foo Fighters) – Warning (Green Day) – Waterloo Sunset (The Kinks) – Weather With You (Crowded House) – Wicked Game (Chris Isaak) – Wild Wood (Paul Weller)

Classic Acoustic Playlist
9806A   VC   ISBN: 1-84328-332-8

Ain't No Sunshine (Bill Withers) – All Tomorrow's Parties (The Velvet Underground) – Alone Again Or (Love) – Another Brick In The Wall Part II (Pink Floyd) – Bad Moon Rising (Creedence Clearwater Revival) – Black Magic Woman (Fleetwood Mac) – Both Sides Now (Joni Mitchell) – Brain Damage/Eclipse (Pink Floyd) – Break On Through (The Doors) – California Dreamin' (The Mamas & The Papas) – Cocaine (Eric Clapton) – Cosmic Dancer (T. Rex) – Crazy Little Thing Called Love (Queen) – Daydream Believer (The Monkees) – Days (The Kinks) – Desperado (The Eagles) – Eight Miles High (The Byrds) – Everybody's Talkin' (Harry Nilsson) – Five Years (David Bowie) – For What It's Worth (Buffalo Springfield) – Fortunate Son (Creedence Clearwater Revival) – Get It On (T. Rex) – Handbags & Gladrags (Rod Stewart) – Happy (The Rolling Stones) – He Ain't Heavy, He's My Brother (The Hollies) – Heroin (The Velvet Underground) – A Horse With No Name (America) – I Feel The Earth Move (Carole King) – It's Only Rock And Roll (The Rolling Stones) – It's Too Late (Carole King) – Itchycoo Park (The Small Faces) – Layla (Eric Clapton) – Leaving On A Jet Plane (John Denver) – Life On Mars (David Bowie) – Light My Fire (The Doors) – London Calling (The Clash) – Long Time Gone (Crosby, Stills & Nash) – Long Train Runnin' (The Doobie Brothers) – The Look Of Love (Dusty Springfield) – Lust For Life (Iggy Pop) – Maggie May (Rod Stewart) – Make Me Smile (Come Up And See Me) (Steve Harley & Cockney Rebel) – Miss You (The Rolling Stones) – Moondance (Van Morrison) – More Than A Feeling (Boston) – Mustang Sally (Wilson Pickett) – New Kid In Town (The Eagles) – Oliver's Army (Elvis Costello) – Pale Blue Eyes (The Velvet Underground) – Perfect Day (Lou Reed) – Silence Is Golden (The Tremeloes) – Sloop John B (The Beach Boys) – Smoke On The Water (Deep Purple) – Space Oddity (David Bowie) – Start Me Up (The Rolling Stones) – Strange Kind Of Woman (Deep Purple) – Stuck In The Middle With You (Stealers Wheel) – Summer In The City (Lovin' Spoonful) – Sunny Afternoon (The Kinks) – Suzanne (Leonard Cohen) – Sweet Home Alabama (Lynyrd Skynyrd) – Tempted (The Squeeze) – Tequila Sunrise (The Eagles) – Turn Turn Turn (The Byrds) – Venus In Furs (The Velvet Underground) – We Gotta Get Out Of This Place (The Animals) – Whiter Shade Of Pale (Procol Harum) – Wuthering Heights (Kate Bush) – You're My Best Friend (Queen) - You've Got A Friend (James Taylor)

Essential Acoustic Strumalong
9808A   BK/CD   ISBN: 1-84328-335-2

All You Good Good People (Embrace) - American English (Idlewild) - The Drugs Don't Work (The Verve) - Grace (Supergrass) - Handbags And Gladrags (Stereophonics) - Hotel Yorba (The White Stripes) - Karma Police (Radiohead) - Love Burns (Black Rebel Motorcycle Club) - Poor Misguided Fool (Starsailor) - Powder Blue (Elbow) - Silent Sigh (Badly Drawn Boy) - Silent To The Dark (The Electric Soft Parade) - Tender (Blur) - There Goes The Fear (Doves) - Underdog (Save Me) (Turin Brakes)

Classic Acoustic Strumalong
9844A   BK/CD   ISBN: 1-84328-397-2

Alone Again Or (Love) - Another Brick In The Wall Part II (Pink Floyd) - Cocaine (Eric Clapton) - Get It On (T. Rex) - Handbags And Gladrags (Rod Stewart) - London Calling (The Clash) - Lust For Life (Iggy Pop) - Make Me Smile (Come Up And See Me) (Steve Harley & Cockney Rebel) - Mustang Sally (Wilson Pickett) - Perfect Day (Lou Reed) - Start Me Up (The Rolling Stones) - Stuck In The Middle With You (Stealers Wheel) - Sunny Afternoon (The Kinks) - Venus In Furs (Velvet Underground) - Whiter Shade Of Pale (Procol Harum)

ailable now in all good music shops

A2